GENERATION SQUEEZED™

A HOLISTIC GUIDE FOR TAKING CARE OF

AGING PARENTS

MORGAN H SMITH JR

For My Family

And

Yours

Table Of Contents

The Bull & Balls

One day, I decided to visit my father, a twenty-minute drive from my house. We sat down in my parents' front patio, where so many times over the years he had given me life advice or just cracked a few jokes. It was a sunny fall day in Coronado, California, with the ever-present ocean breeze and the occasional ship horn claiming its passage in the San Diego Bay. Sitting in the sun with my dad and enjoying the moment, I was tempted to just let it pass and pretend everything was okay. But it wasn't. His dementia had gotten to the point where he could be a danger to himself and others if he was out on the roads; something needed to give before it broke. Because of my love and respect for him, I was committed to help, as hard as it was. I was really worried there would be a lot of pushback, but mostly I felt bad for taking away one of the main things that gave him a sense of control and freedom.

"Dad, you understand you're having a more difficult time with your memory, don't you'"

"Yea. Ha ha. Jeez. Getting old ain't for sissies. But I'm doing all right, son, don't you worry about me. I'm happy."

"Well dad, I know you're happy and that's great. But do you remember when you got lost the other day driving around town?"

"Did I? Ha ha. No, I don't remember. Really?"

"Yep."

"Jeez, that's, well, ha ha, really?"

"Yes really. Mom and I want you to be safe and I don't want you getting in an accident where you might hurt someone else, so it's really time you stopped driving. It's for your safety and everyone else's, so I'm going to have to take your keys away and no more driving."

There was a pause as he looked at me, trying to grasp the full context of what I had just said. Inside, I was fighting the anxiety and guilt, trying to keep myself together. Trying to keep it light and breezy when in actuality I felt the weight of my entire life squeezing my heart and head. He stopped and looked at me. For a moment, I did not think he fully comprehended what I was suggesting. I also worried he might blow up and start yelling and tell me to take a hike. Then he looked at me, and very innocently said, "It's all right son. I understand."

Silence. I just stared at him for a moment making sure I heard his words correctly. And then boom! That's when all of that anxiety, fear, and guilt just washed away. That's when I realized I was really doing the good work in life—helping my father—which was helping my mother, my sister, and myself be happy and give us peace of mind. That moment gave me supreme steadfast confidence that I should continue the path I was on.

That was a transformative moment for me, but as I later found out, despite this small victory, there were many, many difficult times to come. Transformative as it was, it was also a very sad moment for me. My father, tough as nails on the outside, softie on the inside, the strong foundation for my life and our family, had just resigned to the fact that he had met his match. And it tore me up inside. Some people who have dementia get very combative and angry, while some are more serene and calm. Thankfully, my father was the latter; I felt at times he was regressing to a boyhood innocence, taking comfort and a sense of safety in his family. Over the years, our relationship had grown from one of father-son to one of friends, with a love that was solid and always there. This day was a marker in my life, as in essence it was a role reversal, where I was the father and he was my young son.

If I wasn't somewhat prepared for this chapter in my life, it's quite possible everything I had worked hard for could have come tumbling down. But, from this moment on, I was able to approach the decline and death of both my parents with an enlightened and informed approach that was full of confidence and commitment.

A final note on this conversation with my dad. After he told me that he understood and was okay with me taking away the car, he sat there for a moment and then looked at me with the old humorous fire in his eyes and said, "You know son, taking away a man's car is like chopping the balls off of a bull." I laughed and cried at the same time and was very happy to have my dad back for that fleeting moment.

New Beginnings. New Endings.

Moving through life, seeing your parents getting older and knowing you'll most likely experience their passing maybe sooner than later, can be a weight on anyone's emotions. Unless you are thick in it right now, you probably don't walk around thinking about this all the time. But it's there, and it will come.

The universe has a beautiful strangeness to it and here's a reminder. When I was going through the decline and death of my parents, I seemed to be running into a lot of people who were going through the same thing I was—the universe confirming its ways to me. Most of them seemed somewhat adrift, lost in the maze of things they had to take care of. And although they might have felt somewhat confident handling certain things, they were unclear about how to take care of the majority of issues, such as legal, financial, taxes, and their own emotions. I realized I was not alone, and most people are, or will soon be, going through the same situation.

Whether or not you've realized it, entering this new phase in your life means you'll have to decide if and how to help your aging and dying parents. You may be daunted by the prospect of doing this—getting the right caretakers, paying the bills, reviewing investments, settling the estate, dealing with siblings, finding those passwords, understanding the importance of powers of attorney, preparing yourself emotionally, and more. The list goes on and seems overwhelming; in fact, it is—especially if you have nowhere to turn or don't feel like talking about it to anyone.

In this book, I will help you help yourself and your family. Through my personal experiences with my parents and my professional experience as a financial advisor helping families facing similar issues, I'm confident you'll gain new insights and tools to help you through this difficult journey.

There are so many things that could go wrong throughout the process; it's very hard to do things on your own and not be informed. Even if you are getting help, you'll want to be informed. We are all under increased demands in today's life, especially if we are taking care of our own households, our relationships, our children, and our jobs. Even if you thought you had the knowledge and expertise to do everything, you could easily stress yourself to the breaking point and have everything else in life that you've worked hard for over the years come crashing down.

Your parents are a reflection of a national issue that will continue to grow. If you define the aging population as those 65 and over you'll see what I mean.

- There is a sizable growth in our aging population the likes of which has never been seen before in the U.S.

- Our aging population is forecast to almost double in the next 40 years to almost 100 million.

- A significant percentage of aging women lived alone in 2018 and these percentages only increase as you look at older age groups.

- The amount of people requiring nursing home care will be close to 2 million in ten years.

- The demand for elder care is also increasing significantly in large part due to cognitive disorders. In 30 years this number could approach 13 million.

But it's not just about your parents. It's also about you. You are a lead character in this story as you (and therefore your children and your legacy) are most likely beneficiaries of your parents' values and at least some of the wealth your parents have built through their lifetimes. And as you might have surmised, the research tells us you are probably unprepared to handle the new complexities of sudden wealth. U.S. Trust recently surveyed high-net-worth individuals with more than $3 million in investable assets to find out how they are preparing the next generation for handling significant wealth.

"Looking at the numbers, 78 percent feel the next generation is not financially responsible enough to handle inheritance," according to Chris Heilmann, U.S. Trust's chief fiduciary executive. He notes 64 percent [of parents] admit they have disclosed little to nothing to their children [you].

The night I took away my father's access to his car, I took some time to reflect on the fact that I had just denied my father a clear and tangible part of his freedom. I was also thinking about all the friends and clients I had spoken with who were going through similar situations. What I saw in their eyes and heard in their voices was a mix of sadness, fear, love, and surrender. They had surrendered to the idea that this would be a painful and difficult process and there was not much they could do about it.

But it doesn't have to be that way. Having been through the death of both my parents and helped my clients go through the same, I found out it doesn't have to be this way at all. There is hope that this could actually be an experience that transforms your life in a very positive and significant way, including enhancing your relationships with your partner, your children, and of course your parents and the life- long memories you'll have of them.

This book is going to explain to you in a very clear and simple manner the many things you'll need to understand and accomplish throughout this process. But I don't just leave it at that. Data and knowledge unto themselves do not make up our lives and our relationships. This book also explores and gives a perspective on your own emotional barriers and the issues that come up with parents and children as well. If there's one thing I've learned in my personal life and professional life as an investment expert, it's that the emotional and behavioral biases and projections we have can have the most negative impact on our future and our results. You need a holistic approach for the best chance of success and happiness.

Let It Ride?

There's a great Seinfeld scene I'll always remember where Kramer, unbeknownst to Jerry, uses Jerry's money to place a high odds bet on the Knicks. If the Knicks beat the Pacers by more than thirty-five points, the bet would pay ten to one. Kramer's logic to using Jerry's money was that Jerry did not have a gambling problem like Kramer did, so it was okay. Sound Kramer logic. Later, Kramer enters Jerry's apartment all fired up and happy because the Knicks won by thirty-seven points and beat the spread for a $1,000 payout. Kramer, shaking in his shoes, tells Jerry: "See, that's a cool G Daddy-O now you gotta let it riiiide."

It's a hilarious scene better watched on the television than read on paper, but it's a good analogy of how people tend to act when things are going well. When everything is status quo and things are going as we expect, we tend to want to let it ride. We are not usually compelled to plan for future events and think about what our lives will be like when things go bad. Why rock the boat when it's smooth sailing?

You may not recognize it fully, but you spend most of your time just reacting to things that happen to you throughout the day. And when I say react, I mean that usually you don't fully understand the reasons behind your reactions, which can have a very significant impact on your life. I'll explore this issue more thoroughly later in this book. When a crisis occurs, people will either tend to just plow ahead, trying to patch up issues until something else in their life breaks, or they will withdraw into a shell of denial. Either of these approaches can affect your life and relationships negatively, often causing fights between siblings and partners. Between action-takers and do-nothings, there is a whole spectrum of personality types and psychological biases that will affect your decision-making. For example, sudden wealth from an inheritance can cause a lot of stress for you and your relationships and might compel you to make decisions you might not have otherwise made.

The problems that might cause you to make bad decisions will also be relevant for your parents as well, albeit with different underlying factors that often occur with aging. Feeling lonely and depressed, they might start trusting strangers they might have otherwise not engaged with in the past. This often leads to elder financial abuse and could put your parents' future and safety in jeopardy. Even a slight decline in mental acuity can have significant consequences as well. There are countless cases across the country where elderly folks have lost their homes because they have either failed to pay or even slightly underpaid their real estate taxes. You will need to be vigilant to help ensure your parents aren't taken advantage of.

As busy adults, we usually deal with issues that arise with our parents reactively. Often, it's because we are truly busy with our family, work, and friends, and we assume everything is fine unless we hear otherwise. We also know parents often don't like to trouble their kids about problems; you may not hear about things until you find out one of them is in the hospital. Other typical solutions you might think are proactive, for example, just looking at your parents' investments or focusing on budgeting without looking at other important factors in the scenario like your emotional health and your family dynamics, are not very effective. You can find information on just about any of these issues on their own, but without integrating them into a holistic approach, you are bound to have numerous unwanted surprises that could prove detrimental to your family's financial, physical, and emotional health.

People falsely think decisions are typically made from having the right information. That perspective is missing the all-important aspect of how greatly emotions affect our decision-making process. We like to think we make decisions based on good research and logic, but that isn't the case at all. Several years ago, neuroscientist Antonio Damasio made a groundbreaking discovery after studying people who had damaged the part of their brain responsible for generating emotions. Prior to their brain damage, these people were socially astute decision-makers. After brain damage to their emotional centers, however, they could not feel emotions, or they had a hard time doing so. No sadness. No happiness. No grief. No guilt. Boy what a way to live. But I think the most interesting aspect of this study is that after damage to the emotional centers in their brain, they could not make decisions, or they had a hard time doing so. For example, they could describe what they should be doing in logical terms, yet they found it very difficult to make even simple decisions, such as what to eat. The revelation here is that if you just try to consume data to find a solution to make decisions, you are fully discarding the emotional influence on your decision-making.

Imagine waking up in the morning and figuring out what to wear. You've taken into consideration the weather, your appointments, and who'll you'll be meeting; how much time you'll spend on your feet; which patterns match; and the feel of each fabric. You've completed a thorough analysis in your mind and yet you stand there in your pajamas staring at your wardrobe unable to make a decision. Well then, perhaps pajamas will work just fine for the day. This would be a typical morning of anyone whose mind could not process emotions. Most of the time, when you are making a decision guided by some kind of logical process, you probably think you are making a wholly rational decision. Decision-making isn't wholly logical, however; it's greatly influenced by our emotions and you'll need to remember this when contemplating your decisions, speaking with your parents, and communicating and taking care of your partner and children. You'll need someone who can communicate a vision to you to bring about discovery and decision-making, rather than just having a go at it. That was my discovery and part of the rationale behind the content of this book.

Going back again to that moment with my father when I had to take the car keys away from him, I was pretty nervous about the whole idea. I wanted to sit there in the sun with him and let it ride. I thought I had the logic set in my mind as to how I could justify everything. Once I got through that moment, I discovered because of that simple decision and act, my family would be, in the long run, happier. I'd be able to focus on my work. I wouldn't bark at my wife or my son. I'd feel good about what I had done for my parents. I also realized that as much logic as I had put into the decision, it was a very emotional decision as well.

My emotional barrier was really the fear of disappointing my father and making everyone in the family unhappy with the arguments and shouting that were sure to come. In this case it didn't come [much], but the significance of the moment is that you have to be anchored in your resolve to make tough decisions.

In my profession as a financial advisor, I was well versed in intergenerational family issues regarding investments, trusts, insurance, and other financially related issues. In my spiritual life, I was well versed in meditation, understanding thought formation and processes, identifying different personality types, and peeling back the onion to find the truth of why people have certain opinions or perspectives. And I was also an F-14 Naval flight officer, having spent years training and then making three deployments on the USS Kitty Hawk, including combat operations in Iraq with approximately 150 carrier landings. I also had the opportunity to teach university students and future Naval officers leadership, management, and engineering systems. There's no better way to learn how to lead and communicate than through a combination of academic inquiry and practical application. But I also learned that the lessons life has to offer never stop.

My experiences as an F-14 Naval flight officer and a teacher of leadership to college students, I knew how to lead, communicate, compartmentalize, and go into "combat mode" to power through both physically and emotionally difficult periods. But after that moment with my dad, I realized I would need to up my game and fill the gaps to enhance my proficiency and increase the probability of a happy and content outcome, despite the fact that the destination I was marching toward was a definitive end to my parents' physical life in this world. I read as much as possible. I spoke to as many professionals as I could. I engaged with people who were going through the same things with their parents. I learned by doing. I crafted expert knowledge and a perspective I think could be helpful to many others such as yourself.

You could choose to just march forward, head down, feet in the mud, step by slogging step. But unless you integrate the knowledge of the practical work that must be done with a reflection of the real emotional aspects of the journey, you'll most likely fail. Getting through the process with a sense of accomplishment and peace of mind could be a real outcome for you. I'm not just talking about momentary happiness, but a well-grounded calming enlightenment that is persistent and unmoved. Capturing this feeling and holding onto it is tough; it can be like trying to pick up a slippery bar of soap. And holding on isn't quite the right descriptor—it's more of a letting go.

If your parents are important to you, their loss will be deeply meaningful. To understand this more clearly, I'll state it another way. If your parents' loss would be deeply meaningful to you, they must be important to you. And someone who is deeply meaningful to you really deserves your best efforts. So if you give it your best, acknowledging you won't be perfect, you'll find a peace and understanding that will help you experience happiness, a contagious essence that will be felt by those around you.

I have an elderly client who was in the early stages of Alzheimer's and there were disagreements and misunderstandings about roles and responsibilities with her children. The children themselves were already stressed with work and taking care of their kids and partners; the added health issues with their single mom (my client) was bringing their stress level to the breaking point. Even though they were miles apart, I was able to pull together several family meetings via conference call and brought in my client's estate planning attorney and her private fiduciary for the discussions as well. After the meetings, the situation among the children went from one of conflicting agendas and misunderstanding to a clearly delineated game plan and an enhanced understanding between them. This happened because I understood the emotional significance of decisions, and I was able to help them to make some of the tougher decisions from a more centered place. This was truly a transformation for their lives and brought them added peace of mind.

Again, most people just take things as they come and hope for the best. In aviation, we call this flying by the seat of your pants. It can work on limited occasions, but in my former line of work as a Naval flight officer, this approach alone can prove deadly. For nearly every evolution in naval aviation, from preflight and takeoff to combat tactics and carrier landings, we have checklists, standard operating procedures, and emergency procedures. We say the emergency procedures we had to memorize were "written in blood," because they were the result of someone dying. If you remember the scene in "Topgun" where Goose was killed from hitting the canopy upon ejection in the F-14, that was the real deal. A normal ejection among other things simply involves pulling the ejection handle. The canopy is jettisoned first by small explosive charges in its rails so the airman doesn't hit it and break his neck when the rocket motors under the ejection seat fire, shooting him clear of the aircraft. Well, we found out the hard way (written in blood) that if you pulled the ejection handle in a flat spin, the pressure above the canopy would not allow it to get clear of the aircraft and the airman would be launched into the canopy in his ejection seat. Thus, in the emergency procedure checklist for a flat spin, if there was no recovery from it, "Canopy — Jettison" was added as an additional step prior to ejecting. It would be a disaster for a pilot to start learning about a flat spin when he's experiencing 6 Gs hanging in his straps spinning out of control toward the ground.

Similarly for you, you don't want to wait until the event is upon you to start learning about the things you'll need to do; it could spell disaster as well. The point being that I have been through what you are going through now or are going to go through soon with your parents. When things start going sideways with your parents, events can unfold very quickly. You'll go from flying through clear blue skies one minute to a fear- inducing flat spin the next and will probably think about pulling the ejection handle. The procedures and steps I'll discuss in this book are a way to ground you in your decision-making so as to navigate your emotions (and those of your family) and the many legal, financial, and logistical issues you'll be faced with. I've advised my clients through these very same circumstances and have been through them myself, twice. In a sense, my book is written in blood as well.

My mom passed away after my father and after I settled the estate and wrapped everything up, I had a sense of peace and accomplishment that I had done right by my parents, my sister, my wife, and my son. I really felt like I had transformed and elevated not only my well being and emotional intelligence, but those around me as well. I felt like I had honored my parents' legacy. I also was able to help the many people I ran into who were going through the same thing and they were very appreciative—so much so that many told me I should write a book. And the rest, as they say, is history.

By having a resource like this book and gleaning the pearls it has to offer, you'll have the opportunity to transform your life and the lives around you. Because at the end of the day, is there anything more important than your family's happiness?

Before The Fall. Decline. End Days.

Over the pages that follow, I'll tell you how to effectively and responsibly take care of your aging parents. Remember that you don't have to be in the middle of it to gain value from the book. If you have a significant amount of foresight, you are reading this book when everything is fine; good on you. The things you learn will help you open the lines of communication with your parents and family, and as things progress, you'll feel like a master of your own destiny. If you've found this book because you realize you are in the moment with your aging parents and need to catch up, and quickly, the book will help you take control with confidence.

I have structured the book into three overall components: Before The Fall, Decline, and End Days. I felt it would be helpful to acknowledge the stages your parents will be living through and provide you with knowledge and insight within the context of these very real stages you will find yourself dealing with. It's all too common these days to be presented with an overload of information, data, research and solutions to help you solve issues. The problem is that the issues you want to understand and solve don't live in a void and are not applicable at every moment throughout the stages you'll find your parents in. Let me capture the essence of these phases for you.

1. Before The Fall: Everything is hunky dory. Status quo. Move along; nothing to see here. As it turns out, there's a lot that can be done during this phase by you and your parents to help ensure their affairs will be taken care of in the future. If you're lucky enough to have these conversations with your parents during this phase, you are ahead of the game. If your parents are already in the next phases, not to worry; you can still get plenty of insight from reading this section.

2. Decline: You turn around one day and realize your father and/or mother is not the steady hand you always knew. What can you do, if anything? How do you address your emotions and difficulties in trying to figure out how much you should help, if even you should? Do they have enough money for caretakers? Insurance? How do you approach them? The tables are now turning from parent to child to child to parent.

3. End Days: The hope you held onto for your parents— that the management of issues and health could sustain itself for some nebulous indefinite period into the future without a significant impact on your life—is gone. Your mom is managing nicely at home with a care provider and you get a call that she slipped and broke her hip and further diagnosis revealed late-stage lung cancer and it's time to clarify end-of-life wishes and get hospice involved. Instantly, the realization that your mom's death is upon you is not something you can escape while falling asleep at night. And then her passing. There is so much to be done despite the weight of your emotions.

When you reflect on the sections of the book, an important theme comes to light: as you and your family progress into each successive phase, the emotional intensity of the situation increases significantly. Sometimes, it is an excruciating long and drawn-out process. Sometimes, you can be in the decline phase for a short period and then with one phone call you suddenly find yourself in the third phase and the emotional intensity and stress of your life can go through the roof. A perfect example is what happened with my mom when she started feeling sick and needed some help and then I received a phone call from her doctor that she had late-stage invasive cancer and had only a couple months to live. So the phases are directly connected, flow through to each other, and will help you get perspective within the context of your personal experience.

Each chapter in the book will provide you with real-world practical solutions from my personal and professional experience. You'll be able to avoid all the mistakes I made. You'll also be able to avoid all the mistakes I've seen other people make through my professional understanding of financial affairs as a financial advisor. Within these chapters, I intertwine insights on how to help yourself through the emotional and psychological issues that in reality can cause many people to be depressed for years and affect them and their families negatively for the rest of their lives. As I said earlier, information in and of itself gets you nowhere. You need context and insight to set a strong rudder for yourself.

Experiencing the decline and death of a parent is a journey that can be full of suffering if you are not prepared or don't have some help. Sometimes, it might not affect you much, but ignoring the issues can make the situation much harder.

Denial rears its head over time and the emotions you repress tend to crawl up from your subconscious and affect your state of mind on a daily level and thus your life. There's something I learned through my Buddhist studies: every moment counts in your overall happiness. Ask yourself what your life is. In one sense, it's simply the culmination of every small moment that adds up to every hour, every day, and every year. That's it. So the moments are very important, as they are the building blocks for your life. I'll also challenge much of the conventional wisdom you might have. For example, most people think when it comes to investing, the older someone gets, the more consertive the investments should be. That's not necessarily the case. "Older" people may still have thirty years left of living and might need their money working hard for them; moving to a more conservative investment portfolio could actually hurt them. It is practically impossible to transition through this journey full of happiness and peace without help and insight.

As we've already explored, your willingness to make tough decisions will be the thing that ultimately ensures you're happier on the other side of having made them. Because of this, what this work promises you is that as you make these decisions and become happier as a result, your relationships will become lighter, your interactions will evolve, and they will become happier as well. Being conscious and strategic about your decision-making is not just a hypothetical concept, but will have a long-lasting and significant positive impact on your life. Just think about what will happen when you are content and happier when you are going through the three phases of helping your parents and after they have passed away. You will be happier. Your family will be happier. You'll have more success at work. You'll have a sense of fulfillment that you've honored your parents' legacy and done the best you can. You can look at your kids and significant others and know you've done the best you can and when it's your turn to experience the final phase of your life, there will be an added sense of peace and understanding of the circle of life. These are all powerful results you can achieve with some help.

Finally, understand this book is not intended to be an exhaustive study of every last thing you need to know, as that would be information overload and counter- productive. There are many subjects of specific and technical nature I will touch on that have hundreds of books and thousands of professionals who make a living specializing in those areas. Consider this book an executive master's class with a holistic perspective that will give you the skills to successfully navigate the coming years, technically and emotionally. You can transform your life from one of potential darkness and mistakes to one of light, happiness, and competency. My promise to you is that by reading this book, you will have a much greater chance of happiness for you and your family.

Before The Fall

As a son or daughter, you will most likely either be compelled by circumstance or presented with the opportunity to help your parents with issues such as declining physical or cognitive health, or both. One of the most difficult things to do is figure out how to bring up the conversation to your parents if they don't bring it up themselves.

The reality of the situation is that the best time to bring up the conversation is when everything is going well—prior to any issues. Great. You are going to ruin a perfectly fine day with the folks—a day dedicated to a purposeful attempt to the avoidance of politics and how to raise your kids or when you are going to get married— messing it up by bringing up death and dying? Come on, we all just want to drink another beer and flip that burger.

Before you go into battle to save the world, understand you'll have a higher success rate winning those battles through knowledge, training, and having a familiarity with the solutions at hand. Before you start trying to help your parents, it's probably best to make sure that *you* have the tools available to manage your own personal emotional issues that will come up.

Personal Inventory

The first accounting that should be done is with yourself. You need to inventory your assets, but I'm not talking about financial assets. Specifically, I want you to ask yourself this question: "What tools do I have to examine, gain insight, and resolve the feelings and emotions in my conscious and subconscious mind?" Simply stated, what do you have in your toolbox to help you solve your issues? If you're drawing a blank, then you will most likely be setting yourself up for an acceleration of some kind of breakdown if you try to shoulder the additional burden of taking care of your parents, not to mention dealing with their death.

You will be tested in many unforeseeable ways in the coming years by the decline of your parents' health. There will be emotional boxes long forgotten in your subconscious that will open up. There will be long-forgotten childhood memories and emotions that will reveal themselves and challenge your perspective on life and family. Some of these could be devastating, but some could be inspirational and give you a new lease and perspective on life. Either way, you'll be on a healthy psychological road if you are prepared and able to examine, gain insight, and resolve these issues.

The thing is, this process is important in life in general, regardless of whether or not you are helping your parents—so get to it.

There is no question that life is full of tragedy and suffering and we are given the option of how to interact with what befalls us. The most important tools we can have are the abilities to examine the thoughts and emotions that come our way, gain insight on them by understanding how they came about (origination), and resolve them with the state of truth as we understand it.

Your tools will be different from everyone else's to some extent. You may approach this process from the direction of an infinite amount of points. You might like to sit on the beach and think. You might be affiliated with a religious institution and pray. You might exercise. You might play guitar. You might get therapy. Some of these things may at the very least provide you with some peace of mind and that's a great start.

But be aware that some of these things may not actually provide you with insight resulting in a better understanding. For example, you or someone you know might be inclined to talk about problems. There's probably some positives from talking to people about things, but *only* talking about problems doesn't do much, if anything, to resolve them. It's actually a great way to trick yourself into thinking you're sorting things out when in fact you might be just advertising your own anxieties and sidestepping the actual work that needs to be done to confront and resolve them. Ultimately, you'll have to get beyond your anxieties and fears, trust yourself, and be the motivating force in your life. Strive for a different alternative. Listen. Read. (Well done!) Learn. Examine. Gain insight. And take action.

If you can get yourself along this path, you'll find the squeeze will lighten up and you'll feel more free and capable to help and thrive in many ways.

Tools to Cope: Personal Story

With that, let me give you some further insight into what I'm referring to. Many years ago in a land far far away, I was in flight school for the U.S. Navy. I wanted to excel, in fact, I wanted to graduate number one to increase my chances of selecting F-14s. For those of you who are interested, the F-14 Tomcat was the featured plane in "Topgun". I was not on the movie bandwagon; that movie was released shortly after I was already on my path—with being the world's greatest fighter as my goal—as an NROTC scholarship student about a year away from commissioning. I actually was a little ticked off that movie came out when it did, as I figured everyone would want to fly Tomcats and selection would get more competitive—and it did.

So back to the flight school story. I studied hard and was doing well and then a personal issue came into play, and for the first time in my life, I was having a hard time sleeping due to self-imposed stress. For example, I found myself falling into a restless sleep at 2:00 a.m. and waking up two hours later for a 5:00 a.m. briefing with a flight instructor that ended with grueling debriefs and graded results. If this went on, I knew I would be performing at a lower level than needed—putting all my hard work to that point and my future dreams at risk. Needless to say, I was very motivated to do something effective—quickly—and it needed to be done totally within myself, as I wanted no one to know about the problems I was having. I'm sure there were a lot of other flight students having similar issues and maybe it wasn't such a big deal, but I wanted to nip it in the bud.

I picked up a little book called *Zen Mind Beginner's Mind* by Shunryu Suzuki and started meditating. At this point, my meditation effort had one goal: calm down my mind so I could sleep. And, it worked.

Fast forward years later, when my uncle (a story for later), Venerable Acharya Buddha Rakkhita, a very respected Theravada Buddhist elder now deceased, invited me to travel to one of his Maha Bodhi temples in Bangalore, India. I would take the monks' precepts, and dive into an intensive learning (Dhamma) and meditative period as a monk. I accepted the invitation and it turned out to be one of the most important experiences of my life.

My days consisted of waking up at about 4:30 a.m. for some temple cleaning, usually consisting of sweeping dirt, followed by morning sitting meditation with the rest of the monks at 5:30 a.m. for about an hour. Personal time then breakfast. Walking meditation. Dhamma talk. Sitting meditation. Lunch. Walking meditation. Sitting meditation—well, you get the picture. No food after noon. Not a big deal. But, no talking, no reading, no TV or movies, etc. This may seem like a minor addition to the agenda, but it has a powerful impact. It *forces* you to be totally within your mind. You cannot run away from your mind by reading or talking to someone. It's there, in your face, and there's no escape.

The basic meditation techniques I employed were Samatha Anapnasati (focusing on the breath to empty and calm the mind), Metta (loving kindness), and Vipassanā (insight). I will defer to Buddhist teachings to cover these in more detail if you're interested, but the technique relevant to this story was the ability acquired through Vipassana—wherein you are challenged to, for example, trace an emotion back to its original pure thought moment and understand how its resulting nature came to fruition in the form of happiness, anxiety, nervousness, anger, etc. If you are able to follow that path and see the transformation, you'll get insight into why you are feeling a certain way or reacting in a certain way. This is very important, as most people go through life believing their reactions are due to external factors, but they're actually a result of the conditioning of their mind—and they never get to the truth of the matter. This is just one small example, but the process can be used in all things in life to gain insight and find the truth.

To that point, one morning at sitting meditation I felt a small pain in my knee. Although relatively limber, I did not grow up sitting cross-legged and I sometimes had to adjust to be comfortable, but mostly I dove deeper into my mind and meditated outside of the pain. My internal conversation went something like this: "Darn. My knee is hurting a little. Okay, back to the breath. But jeez, I've got what about another forty-five minutes of this? And then more later today? And what, how many more weeks of this? Seriously? I shaved my head and am in a yellow robe sitting in a temple halfway around the world from my life? WHAT AM I DOING???"

It was "what am I doing?" that invaded the deepest darkest depths of my fears and subconscious, and it possessed so much force that my entire foundation of life as I knew it broke apart as if shattered by a powerful earthquake. I was broke. I could not move. I had lost my compass at that moment. Vertigo. I sat there and felt the waves of sadness and fear wash over me until the end of meditation, when I sucked it up and went to my room. Later that morning, I went to Acharya and told him about my experience; as I spoke, tears came from eyes and I was shaking. He got a big smile on his face, patted me on the shoulder, chuckled a little, and said, "You're going to be all right. Just think about what happened." He then turned around and walked off.

Strangely enough, that worked. At least it worked enough to snap me out of my funk so I could think about what happened. Here was my "insight." To sum it up, the pain in my knee caused me to lose my entire foundation in life. Let me say that again. A pain in my knee caused me to lose my entire foundation in life. It's pretty scary to realize a mundane little thing in your day like a pain in the knee, a smell, a word spoken, a song, an email—anything—can trigger a chain of subconscious thoughts you don't realize are occurring into a powerful change in your state of mind. With the ability to identify the source or the trigger for that chain reaction, I was able to gain insight into the true nature of what had happened and resolve the issue. Wow, a pain in my knee caused all of that? It's pretty scary to think that throughout the day we are reacting to things in ways we don't even understand. Had I not had the ability to have this insight, I might have been stuck in a long-term funk or depression and lost my way.

The purpose of sharing this story is not to imply that Vipassanā meditation is the best methodology for you to gain insight, just that you *will need something* in your life that will help you understand and manage all the emotions that will come at you from the unlit regions of your mind as you watch your parents slowly die before your eyes.

Here's an additional nugget of understanding to what happens with our emotions when dealing with aging parents, offered as it relates to the story I just told. Later that day, Acharya sat me down and explained what happens to the mind when you do intensive meditation and self-reflection. Consider that your mind works on essentially two levels, the conscious and the unconscious. If you think of it like a jar of water, over time you build up a lot of sediment at the bottom (unconscious mind). The conscious mind (top of the jar) is relatively clear—so you seem to be okay—but sitting in the depths of your mind is a whole bunch of junk that has yet to be resolved. Part of the goal of any spiritual practice and meditation is to clear the mind. But the thing is, the process of clearing the mind involves a disruption of the precarious equilibrium that exists; when you shake the "jar," the sediment becomes interspersed throughout the mind and can cause a lot of negative psychological responses.

That, according to Acharya, was exactly what I had experienced. Although at the time it was quite a negative experience, it was a necessary part of the process. My belief is that when you have emotional trauma in your life, including moments that will arise when caring for aging parents, the same thing occurs—so be wary and mindful of this. Acharya explained it's important to have someone who understands mental factors and psychology to escort people off the ledge when these moments occur. He did this with me, knowing exactly what would work. So, the moral of the story is, have someone you can turn to as your jar is shaken; it may mean the difference between insight and a dark path forward.

In summary, I want you to explore ways in which you and you alone can manage and resolve issues that come your way. Many of the things we do, such as talking to people about our problems, are just diversions and don't really transform and resolve issues. Many of the techniques out there can be learned, much like techniques taught in flight school. Without learning them, chances are your plane will crash. But let's also accept that many of us are genetically and psychologically inclined to be affected more or less by stressful situations. For example, you'll find one of the most important traits cited by SEALs as a predictor of successful completion of their training is an intangible, unteachable belief that they will just not quit or give up. That kind of fortitude varies from person to person and there's not too much we can do about it.

One final note is that I am not a licensed psychologist or medical doctor. If you find yourself having serious mental or physical conditions as a result of the stresses in life, there may be chemical imbalances or other issues that cannot be treated merely through some of the techniques I mentioned, so don't be shy in seeking a medical opinion, if necessary.

Stress Factors

Everyone experiences stress in their lives, so it's important to understand a little bit about the underlying physiological initiators and effects of stress. In reality, stress is a mental reaction to external factors. Mental stress does not exist as a phenomenon unto itself, but must be created by our bodies and minds. To illustrate this point, imagine there are two people standing on the edge of a cliff. One person is scared of heights. The other person has lived walking cliffside trails and is completely comfortable. Here you have two people with the same external inputs. The scared person might be freaking out entirely with a heightened heart rate, shaking, sweating, and might even pass out. Meanwhile, the other person is calm and smiling, enjoying the beautiful view. So, stress is a reaction, sometimes healthy, oftentimes unhealthy, to external factors.

It is well known in scientific fields that the hormone cortisol is released in response to stress and fear. Cortisol is a hormone produced in the brain, specifically in the adrenal cortex within the adrenal gland. The release of cortisol has many positive aspects for normal stress levels, such as preventing the release of substances in the body that cause inflammation.

However, prolonged elevated cortisol levels (stress) can wreak havoc on the body. People have a higher risk for depression and a lower life expectancy with chronic stress and elevated cortisol levels. Studies have also shown that a possible trigger for mental illness includes increased cortisol levels.

Higher cortisol levels were also found to be associated with physical changes in the brain that are often seen as precursors to Alzheimer's disease and other forms of dementia, according to a study published in the October 2019 online issue of *Neurology*®.

Imagine getting so stressed about helping your parents that *you* get depressed, become mentally ill, and die early. Not only is this possible, but it's probably more common than we might want to believe. The irony and sadness in this scenario is motivation enough not to get caught in that trap. Simply put: know your enemy.

As it turns out, cortisol has in fact been referred to as public enemy number 1, but there are some pretty easy ways to help lower your cortisol levels:

- Cardio exercise like running and swimming

- Engaging with family and friends

- Meditating

- Listening to music

- Laughing

Weave these activities into your daily life to help you control your stress regardless of whether or not you are helping out your parents. When the time comes, they will be excellent friends to fall back on.

Why Take Care of Your Parents?

I was speaking with a friend the other day. She's a trooper who's been taking care of her father with commitment, patience, and humor. It's in her nature. Her father is declining cognitively and needs help with many daily activities. He needs help eating, and of course needs help with the calls of nature as a result of his eating. Even in his cognitively damaged state of mind, he just can't seem to get over the hump of getting to it in the bathroom with his daughter there helping. He'll just stand there and do nothing rather than display his private functions to his well-intentioned daughter.

Sometimes stubborn just sticks around. Her descriptors were much more colorful than what I've just written and we were having a good laugh with a shared understanding of the love underlying the process. She then took a turn and told me how the most difficult thing in life has been watching her dad slowly, inch by inch, minute by excruciating minute, slide down the slow, frustrating, and painful path toward death. She explained it as an emotionally painful and morbid watching of paint as it dries. And that, my friends, is a reality of the situation. And quite frankly, it's your choice on how involved you want to or can be.

Let's pause for a moment and ask either the most obvious question or something you've never even contemplated: Why take care of your parents?

There really is no good answer and everyone will have a different perspective, so one thing I can do to help is give you mine. I suppose I can sum up my reasons with two words: love and honor. It's as simple as that. I did not feel obligated to help them. They did not make me feel like I owed them for all the things they did for me. In reality, we all have our lives and are responsible for ourselves, and I very well could have been living halfway around the world and unable to help them. However, I know I would have had regrets if I did not have the opportunity to help them. Now let's explore this issue a little more.

Moral—As a person, you can make the moral argument that you are not obligated to help anyone and be guided by your philosophical and spiritual foundations on this. As the saying goes, we don't choose our family and there are plenty of people in the world who have horrible parents and are less eager if not adamantly opposed to helping them.

Legal—As a parent, you not only have a moral obligation to help your children, but a legal obligation as well. There are different laws in different states that govern parental rights and responsibilities but parents are generally the individuals that have legal custody of their children. A parent must serve the child's best interests by at least meeting their basic needs and a financial duty that usually continues until the child is eighteen years old or graduates from high school with exceptions for instances where a child has special needs.

That's the general framework for parents' obligations to children, barring any extenuating circumstances where a court may alter a parent's rights and responsibilities in cases such as divorce, abuse, and neglect.

The question for us now is, what, if any, legal responsibilities do adult children have to their parents? At first thought, you might think there are none; you're all adults and to each his own.

Imagine one day you receive a letter stating that you are financially responsible for a parent's care facility stay, and if you don't pay $60,000, you'll be sued. If you think that sounds crazy, I wouldn't disagree with you, but unfortunately it's within the realm of possibilities.

Filial—This responsibility is defined as a duty owed by an adult child for his parents' necessities of life. So what happens when a parent in need of long-term healthcare is unable to pay for it? Many states have laws that require adult children to be financially responsible for their parents' necessities of life when the parents don't have the means to pay for them on their own.

As of the time of this writing, filial responsibility laws are on the books of twenty-nine states. In a relatively recent case (*Health Care & Retirement Corporation of America v. Pittas* [Pa. Super. Ct., No. 536 EDA 2011, May 7, 2012]), the court deemed that a son should pay $93,000 for care received by his mother at a Pennsylvania skilled nursing facility.

So it's both a somewhat obscure legal concept and an unsettling one, knowing you could be on the hook financially for your parents. Regardless of the legal veracity of these filial responsibility laws, perhaps it could be a little added ammunition for you when you're speaking with your parents about helping you help them.

How to Approach Parents

The way you approach your parents with this sensitive subject has to be thoughtful and the timing has to be right. If communicated the wrong way, a parent might hear, "Mom, Dad, how much money have you saved up and when do I get it?" Somehow, you have to try to convert the perceived message to, "Mom, Dad, I want to help in any way I can throughout the later stages of your lives. Would it be okay if we discuss how you've set up your affairs so I can better help?"

As I mentioned before, when a parent passes away, there tends to be a paradigm shift in your perspective of life and death. Where once mortality was a vague prospect that happened to older people, it can now become a clear and present inevitability. After my father's father passed away, he put together his "Toes Up" file and ensured I went through it with him and knew where everything was. It was a low-tech paper folder with handwritten notes, but the effort and acknowledgment were there.

If your parent(s) are willing to discuss the subject, you have an open path to setting things right in the future. If not, you have a few choices:

- Walk away and forget about it.

- Wait until an event in their lives changes their position.

- Give it some time and bring up the matter again.

- Talk to one of your parents' close friends/confidants to try and influence them to change their stance.

- Wait until there is a medical prognosis deeming them mentally unfit to manage their affairs

One effective way to get your parent(s) to open up is with the following question: *"What do you want your legacy to be after you pass away?"* Parents often don't like being a burden or they just need some encouragement to think long term. It's helpful to remind them that their legacy to their family and community can be important. Inspire them to think bigger because they are important to you and everyone around them. Their legacy and deeds can be helpful and inspiring to generations even after they have passed away. This angle might help you get them to consider more planning and preparedness that might otherwise not occur. If they respond with something like, "It's all in the will; don't worry about it," remind them that with that attitude, they're most likely going to make everyone's life more difficult—perhaps leading to fights—and that's not what they want for the family and their legacy. That's about as close to the water you can bring that horse and maybe after some reflection on a hot day, they'll drink and get to it.

Parents' Response—When Kids Try To Help

One of the most contentious times is when you approach your parents to offer help. Some of you might be scared or have some anxiety even thinking about this, and rightly so.

Many parents will be stubborn, set in their ways, and very private—so they may react negatively to the proposition of discussing their game plan for the future with you. Some parents will tell you to take a hike and get very upset. Some will deflect and say they're taking care of it. Many will just not want to bother anyone. Some will actually be proactive and involve their kids early on with these discussions and have family meetings.

In reality, your parents generally have no obligation whatsoever to share information with you or even name you as beneficiary of their assets. It's all theirs. Period. (Of course, barring any transfers made to irrevocable trusts, etc., but more on that later.) The point is, if they are mentally competent, your parents can spend everything they own on an endless trip around the world or gift everything to a charity—and that would be fully their right.

Much of the pushback you might get is really due to control issues. It's often the daily routines of paying bills, driving the car, cooking food, etc. that provide purpose to lives in homes that were once full of kids, work, and friends. People in general, and older folks especially, have a hard time contemplating a path to less control of their lives, much less giving up control.

In actuality, they can have full control with trusts and wills.

Fear vs Being Afraid

I read a lot. Everyone has a unique perspective and you never know where it's going to come from. It could be Keith Richards' book, *Life* or Marcus Luttrell's book, *Service: A Navy Seal At War*. If you don't know who Keith Richards is, I've got nothing for you. Let's just say he's the riff master for the Rolling Stones and as a guitarist I've studied his riffs with emphasis on the years between 1968 and 1973, when his Gram Parsons-inspired guitar playing propelled the Stones through their golden years.

If you don't know Marcus Luttrell (and his fellow warriors who he's brought to light), you should. He's probably best known by the public via his recounting of Operation Redwing in his book, *Lone Survivor*, which became a motion picture as well. A cursory reading of his bio will most likely leave you with the impression that he is a decorated U.S. Navy SEAL. That's enough in and of itself, and while you might not see much more, there is—much more.

As I've mentioned before, I grew up in Coronado. As kids, we were always up at O-Dark early surfing and we'd see SEALs running down the beach with their boats on their heads. It didn't look like much fun. But since then, I've always felt something special about those guys; they were part of my social fabric. I went on a different path in the Navy as an F-14 Tomcat naval flight officer and didn't cross paths with them professionally until I was teaching as an assistant professor of naval science at the NROTC program at the University of San Diego. I had one SEAL sniper student who was in the process of becoming an officer. I was a senior lieutenant at that time and remember my first counseling session with him. Keep in mind we kept a pretty tight leash on our midshipmen, as we wanted them to succeed, and there are plenty of opportunities to get sidetracked (fail) in college. So, I had a "lowly" midshipman in my office, with a SEAL Trident on his chest. How to handle that? I realized he didn't need me, unless he did. And he'd let me know if he did. So I told him I was going to let him take care of his business on his own and he should let me know if he needed anything. I never did that for any other midshipman, but that's how much respect I had for those guys.

Fast forward many years later and I just finished reading Marcus Luttrell's second book, Service: A Navy SEAL At War. I'll admit it's one of the best books I've ever read—not merely because of the incredible action presented in operations, but the insights into the hearts and minds of people during chaos and stress. Loyalty, love, and a never-quit attitude translate very well to life in general if given enough thought.

Two sentences in the book that hit me like a laser are worth sharing in the context of taking care of aging and dying parents.

"Fear is a force that sharpens your senses. Being afraid is a state of paralysis in which you can't do anything." —Marcus Luttrell

I'd never thought of the distinction between fear and being afraid in this way and it's both brutal and brilliant at the same time. The words speak for themselves, so I won't pontificate on them much. I'll just point out that it's very easy to be afraid when you're confronting the prospects of walking with your mom or dad down the path to their certain death. My hope is that this book will help you to not be afraid of the process, as paralysis is a real consequence many people in this situation experience. If there is any "negative" emotion, let it be fear, understanding it is really a force that can bring strength and resolve.

Family Meetings

How many times has your family sat down together to talk about a specific agenda? For many families, the answer is zero. This is really a shame, as there is so much wisdom to be shared between family members and countless opportunities to clear up misunderstandings. With modern technology, we've almost lost the art of gathering around the fire to share stories, ideas, and dreams, as people tend to be absorbed in their own personal and techno-bubbles. Having a family under the same roof might seem like it will last forever, but it's in fact a moment in life that will dissipate quickly as children get older and move on.

A family meeting can be as formal or casual as you want. In essence, a family dinner is a family meeting, but then how often these days do families get to eat together?

In the context of what we are discussing, a family meeting can be more narrowly defined as an opportunity for the parent(s) to discuss their legacy with their children, educate them on financial matters, and give them an opportunity to be involved in concerns such as a family business or charity. Family meetings in this context have often been traditionally expected to occur with very wealthy families that have multiple businesses, trusts, and complex investment and legal affairs. Typically, a "Family Office" is set up by the parents with in-house attorneys and advisors hired by the family to be stewards of their affairs. It also provides some adult supervision and predefined limitations on children who might be less inclined to be responsible and carry on with the legacy intents of their wealthy parents.

But, family meetings need not be limited to the wealthiest families nor do they need to be limited to what parents want to talk about, but can be a true forum with everyone involved. I've always encouraged all families to consider family meetings, at the very least to give parents an opportunity to reveal their plans and intent when they are in decline and after they have passed away. Possible discussion points are how assets will be distributed, medical end-of-life directives, where documents are located, who to contact, etc. It's also an opportunity for parents to ask questions of their children regarding their desires and goals. There might be a situation, for example, where parents thought giving a home to each child was ideal and they come to find out one of the children has no desire whatsoever to live in the area where the home is located and prefers cash for other reasons, such as starting a business.

An ideal approach is to encourage your parents to have a family meeting prior to a decline in health so they can discuss their ideas regarding their estate. This gives them the opportunity to make any changes to wills, revocable trusts, and other documents after getting feedback from their children. Once everything is in place, ongoing family meetings can occur to clarify the changes and provide updates as investments change.

A best practice for a family meeting is to have a professional referee involved, like a financial advisor, to help set the agenda, keep the conversation on track, and clarify any misconceptions participants might have. An estate planning attorney or trust fiduciary is also a great addition to the team to clarify any legal issues regarding roles and responsibilities. Good agenda items are parents clarifying the goals and values behind their intentions, where their important documents are located, what medications they are currently on, and their wishes and desires when they pass away. Of course, anything can be on the table for discussion and if it's not, it will probably come up sooner rather than later. There also might be areas you want to discuss, but for whatever reason your parents do not. In that instance, if you feel it's important, just state your case, get perspective from the professional referee, and let the chips fall where they may. Remember, these meetings are not intended to end with perfect resolutions and most likely someone will be less than happy or satisfied, but my opinion is that the more truth that can come out during the meetings, the better everyone will be in the long run.

Family meetings might be very revealing, especially when conducted with a financial advisor. You might have a sibling who is full of greed and has alternate plans. If that's the case, his or her character will most likely be revealed to everyone at the meetings. But, once that sibling understands there is a well-thought-out and airtight plan developed by professionals, he or she will probably be less inclined to try to take advantage of the situation which leads to less quarrels in the future.

There might be a new spouse in the mix if one or both of your parents have divorced and remarried. It's quite possible you thought you might be receiving a significant amount of assets from your father, but find out his new spouse is getting everything and she doesn't much like you. This happens all the time and as long as your father is of sound mind and barring any other extenuating circumstances, there's not much you can do about.

As you can see, the list of unsatisfied players in this environment can expand significantly if you take into account your parents' siblings, in-laws, business partners, etc. At the end of the day, your parents are free to act as they wish and if that means cutting everyone off and spending everything on life experiences or charity, that is within the realm of possibilities and you'll just have to accept it. If for some reason there is a real concern about fraud or elder abuse, by all means contact an attorney and investigate things more thoroughly and professionally instead of charging head first with personal confrontations, which can just exacerbate the problem.

Another practical effect of family meetings is that they will help in reducing the probability of lawsuits and legal action among family members. If you actually like the idea of confrontation and long drawn out legal procedures, then all the power to you and stay away from me. Most sane people I know don't get excited about the prospect of being in lengthy legal proceedings with a family member. If in a family meeting everyone becomes more aware of what the parents' legal wishes are, they will be less likely to be taken advantage of and less likely to try and take advantage of someone else, knowing they are informed. Although not an absolute recipe for peace, love, and understanding, family meetings might help your family avoid full throttle warfare. I have known people who have been in legal proceedings with siblings for over a decade, a decidedly unhealthy situation.

Remember, the purpose of this book is to help give you long-lasting peace of mind through what can be a very tumultuous period in your life. I think family meetings can go a long way in avoiding the prospects of years-long litigation among family members, a brutal experience that can take its toll on everyone involved and literally destroy families.

Siblings

"The greatest gift our parents ever gave us was each other."

"Siblings: your only enemy you can't live without."

If you have siblings, I don't know which of the above quotes best applies to you, but it's safe to say sibling relationships often go through difficult periods. Issues such as jealousy due to perceived preferential treatment are a common cause of sibling rivalry that is sometimes never resolved.

At the end of the day, siblings are like branches of a tree that grow in different directions but have the same roots. That reality might make you feel good that you have someone with a common history and bond, or you might feel stuck or overshadowed in the family dynamic. Either way, you will most likely have to contend with the prospects of increased involvement and communication with your siblings when things go bad for your parents.

If your parents have set things up correctly and have the financial resources to have had everything taken care of, there might be minimal need for siblings to get involved. But, even if the need is not necessary, some might be inclined to get very involved anyway.

I'm lucky my sister and I have always had a very good relationship. I attribute this to the idea that we've generally had a solid foundation, emotional maturity, and our own pursuits on our spiritual journeys.

She was integral in helping me sort out issues and emotions, and she traveled to be there physically with my parents when she could. But it wasn't easy for her. When you live off-grid in the country with animals and a constant need for upkeep and repair of, well, everything, it's a significant logistical nightmare to leave for a couple days, much less a couple weeks. She is also not keen on flying, so her train and bus rides would result in a trip of close to twenty-four hours to get to Coronado.

It was my sister who was there through the last days with my mom, facing her death moment by moment, through the pain and breathing difficulties, watching her wither away until the day she passed. There is nothing easy about it, but my sister went through it with grace and determination.

In my mind, there was no good to her relative isolation, nor was there any bad to it. It just was what it was and I trusted her to make the right decisions for her, her family, and our parents. And that's an important point to remember when dealing with siblings—it will be easier for some than others to help. Life and its ongoing demands will not stop for anyone to afford you the freedom to invest all your energy into your parents. You can choose to drop everything in your life to help, or you can choose to drop nothing and watch from afar. Each choice has its own consequences, positive and negative, that you'll have a reckoning with at some point in the future.

This is also an important point for parents to consider. Perhaps it's best to plan on getting no help from your children or anyone else, and then whatever help does come is just a bonus and a blessing. As the saying goes, sometimes the best help is learning there's no help at all.

Siblings are at different stages of their life, will have different perspectives of roles and responsibility, and will have different levels of spiritual and emotional intelligence. It's no secret that siblings can go through periods of intense conflict and there tends to be one or two who are more responsible than others. It's also the case that you might have siblings who have gotten themselves into financial difficulty or are being pressured by spouses to get some more money somewhere. Some will be trustworthy givers, some will be evil takers. There are many cases involving siblings who have actually sued their parents prior to their deaths in an effort to gain more financially or have more control. And, when parents have children with multiple partners—due perhaps to divorce and remarriage—the dynamics of these extended families are often more dysfunctional.

Generally, as I already noted, deceased parents have no obligation to leave anything to their children. In fact, nearly every state allows parents to completely disown their children in a will. If a parent did not leave a will, however, children may have rights to assets as dictated by state law. Additionally, children are considered "interested persons," meaning they have a right to contest a parent's will if they have valid grounds. Generally, children are entitled to receive whatever their parent bequeaths them in a last will and testament. The only time a bequeath to children may be invalid is if the parent left more to her children than she is allowed to by law. For example, in community property states, marital assets are considered equally owned by both spouses. Thus, a surviving spouse is entitled to a certain portion of the marital estate; a deceased spouse cannot disinherit a spouse entirely or leave more than what she owned to her children in a will. If a parent left a will and left out her child but did not explicitly disinherit the child, the child may have a right to an inheritance because it may be assumed the parent omitted the child by accident.

With all of this in mind, you will have to become the expert and ultimately decide how and who to deal with when it comes to your siblings. Hopefully, your parents will have set up their affairs in a way that clears up any misunderstandings so your relationships are enhanced through the journey.

Financial Plan

It is highly recommended that your parents have a comprehensive financial analysis in place that includes all assets, spending assumptions, and investment growth rates. In addition, a probability analysis should be conducted on the likelihood of not running out of money for the surviving spouse's lifetime given different scenarios.

One day, you may find yourself quickly needing to provide help or input regarding your parents' estate—or even manage it. And many of you might have little or no experience doing this. Worse yet, maybe you've dabbled in the stock market and have picked some winners or you have your own system that seems to work. I could write an entire book on investing and I might in fact do that someday, but I'll keep it simple with some underlying principles to remember.

What's important for you to understand is that when you're getting any kind of advice, you want to get it from someone who's not conflicted. What does this mean? It means you don't want to get advice from someone who's getting paid (or better paid) to sell you a particular product or solution. When you're working with commissioned advisors, their solutions can be in their best interest rather than yours. So, I always advise that you seek out a fee-*only* (not fee-*based*) financial advisor. These are advisors who get paid by their clients *only*. Since they're not getting paid (or paid better) to sell you anything in particular, you tend to get better solutions, in your best interest, at a lower cost. A great resource to find a fee-only advisor is the National Association of Professional Financial Advisors (NAPFA), the country's leading professional association of fee-only financial advisors.

It's really important not only to get advice, but to get advice from the right people, especially when it comes to something critically important to your parents as their financial future. You may find yourself having to assess your parents' current financial plan and advisor to get a second opinion. Or, your parents might not have a plan and need to get one in place. How do you find the right financial advisor you can trust to deliver? You need to be educated and ask the right questions. Here are some critical questions to ask financial advisors you are considering to retail:

1. <u>What licenses, credentials, or other certifications do you have?</u>

   Not every person who calls themselves a "financial advisor" or "financial planner" has equal education, responsibilities, or ethical requirements. In fact, there is no legal licensing requirement to call yourself a financial advisor or financial planner. Anyone can call themselves a financial advisor or financial planner, which means you should vet anyone who will be potentially guiding your financial future

   To start, look for someone who has attained a designation of advanced training. The four designations that are the most highly regarded are Certified Financial Planner, Chartered Financial Consultant, Certified Public Accountant and Personal Financial Specialist.

   By having at least one of these designations, the advisor will have demonstrated some core competencies. To earn the Certified Financial

Planner (CFP®) designation, the individual must pass a comprehensive board examination.

Individuals who work for stock brokerage firms are licensed as registered representatives. They must pass certain multiple choice tests that cover investments like stocks, bonds, options, and other investment products to sell these investments to the public. Oftentimes, the registered representatives will have an insurance license so they can also sell insurance products. No financial planning exams or training is required.

2. <u>Are you required by law to put my interests ahead of your own?</u>

This is a "gotcha" question. How the advisor you are interviewing answers this question will tell you a lot about him or her.

Fee-only advisors work for Registered Investment Advisory firms, not insurance companies, stock brokerage firms, or banks.

If the advisor you are speaking with tells you they have a legal obligation to put your interests ahead of their own and they work for a stock brokerage firm, bank or insurance company—well, they may not be telling you the truth.

Suitability offers some protection, but it is not the gold standard. Suitability means the advisor only has to reasonably believe any recommendations made are suitable for clients, in terms of the client's financial needs, objectives, and unique circumstances. A key distinction in loyalty is also important because the first duty of advisors who work at stock brokerage firms, banks, and insurance companies is to their employer, not to their client.

This is a very important point, considering so many people are calling themselves "financial advisors" and financial planners" these days. The fact that literally anyone from your local insurance agent to your postal worker can use these terms has rendered them meaningless for anyone looking for unbiased advice.

3.   What services do you/does your firm provide?

Some advisors provide you advice on your investments or insurance while others offer comprehensive financial planning centered around retirement, insurance, estate planning, tax planning, and charitable giving, along with investment management.

4.   What is your investment approach?

Make sure the advisor has an investment philosophy that is compatible with your goals and risk tolerance.

Ask them how they determine what investments to use and how much risk you should take on in your particular situation.

If you don't understand what they are talking about, it might be best to find someone who can explain what they are doing in a language you can understand and you are comfortable with.

5. <u>How and how much do you charge for your services?</u>

If you don't see this information on the advisor's website, make sure you ask how you would be charged. Ask for a copy of any agreement you will need to sign.

Not only should you know how much the service will cost you, but it can help you determine whether the advisor has an incentive to sell you certain products or investments.

6. <u>What is the difference between fee-based and fee-only compensation?</u>

This gets confusing. Because they sound similar, consumers tend to think they are the same thing. In fact, they couldn't be more different.

Fee-only compensation is the most straightforward form of compensation. Fee-only advisors are only paid based on a percentage of their clients' assets and/or on an hourly basis. Fee-only advisors receive no other compensation from any other source. This allows them to review each alternative solution, and then provide their clients with an unbiased opinion as to the pros and cons of each.

Fee-based compensation means the advisor can be paid either a percentage of the client's assets (like the fee-only advisor) or a commission or both.

7. What are your professional affiliations?

The National Association of Personal Financial Advisors (NAPFA) is the country's leading professional organization for fee-only advisors. It has 2,400 members. The Financial Planning Association is the largest membership organization for Certified Financial Planner® professionals, with over 100 chapters nationwide.

8. Have you ever been disciplined by the SEC or FINRA?

The Securities Exchange Commission (SEC) regulates Registered Investment Advisory (RIA) firms, while the Financial Industry Regulatory Association (FINRA) regulates the stock brokerage industry and is overseen by the SEC.

You can check out advisors who work for RIA firms by going to the SEC website: sec.gov/investor/brokers.htm.

To research advisors who work for stock brokerage firms, go to BrokerCheck.com.

When it comes to investing in a securities portfolio consisting of stocks and bonds that's a nest egg for your parents, or money they cannot afford to lose, there are a few golden principles to follow. Before I speak about investing in general it is important to clarify a *disclaimer for all of the investment discussion in this book in that the indexes I discuss are not available for direct investment and performance does not reflect expenses of an actual portfolio and, that past performance is not a guarantee of future results.*

Approach the investment decisions with a concept that you already know, namely; nobody can predict the future. You know this! Don't you? Everyone does. Yet, investors still think they or someone they hire has some special secret sauce, special insight, or a proven system, that can...wait for it....predict the future. Or maybe it's decades of experience, a Ph.D., a great ten-year track record, or something that attests to their ability to select which stocks (or sector, or country) are going to be the best to buy for future performance. In other words, they're predicting the future. The secret is, they don't really know. Nobody knows. So don't go with an investment philosophy that deludes itself into thinking it can predict the future, especially consistently over days, weeks, years, and decades. Investors can be very successful with relatively lower risk using the appropriate investment strategy that acknowledges this fact.

If you want all the best stocks but want none of the bad stocks in your portfolio, what strategy should you use to accomplish this? Well, there is none. There has been no proof that anyone can consistently over decades select only the good stocks. And of course, any hurdle in an investment strategy must be that the value received is greater than the cost. You add this into the equation and things just get harder. So the goal is not the right investment goal. The "goal" can be defined in several different ways.

Only take risks that historically investors have been rewarded for. For example, if you pick a stock, you may or may not be rewarded with that investment choice. The company's stock could perform extremely well or it may completely fail; you just don't know. But if you look at the broad stock market index returns with at least decades of historical information, you'll find they have positive returns. The case can be clearly made that the risks of the global markets have produced rewards over time.

Invest in such a way that you lower the probability that your parent will not run out of money over an assumed lifetime. One way we in the financial planning world do this is not to assume a constant rate of return every year, say 6 percent, for example. We know that year-by-year your investment portfolio will have a different return, which can actually give you much different results than assuming the same rate of return every year. One way we can get a perspective on this is to use a Monte Carlo Analysis, which assumes many different return possibilities every year and comes up with a statistical analysis of the expected returns over time. This, in my opinion, is a better way to forecast a retirement strategy.

Let's go back to my statement that wanting all of the good stocks but none of the bad stocks in your portfolio is not the right goal. I said this because no one has had the perfect crystal ball. So, for nest egg money, funds you cannot afford to lose, your goal should simply be to have as many of the good companies in your portfolio and not worry about whether or not you'll have the bad companies in there as well. As a matter of fact, if you do it correctly, you'll be guaranteed to have bad companies in your portfolio. It's just that the effect of the best companies in your portfolio will override the effect of the bad companies, over time.

Let me give you an example. Let's say you had just about all of the listed stocks in the world sitting in a basket in front of you. Of course, this will include not only the best performing stars of the future, but also the laggards and the companies that will fail.

So you've got a basket that you can say is a robust representation of the global stock markets. Now let's say, starting in 1994 until 2015, at the end of each year, you measured the performance of your basket. And then you averaged all of those rates' average compound return. Do you know what your return would be? It would be approximately **7.2 percent**. Hmmm. Is that good? It doesn't sound too exciting, but not bad. Let's look at it from a total return perspective by way of a simple future value calculator you can find and look for yourself at calculator.net. If you input twenty-one years as the investment period at 7.2 percent, $1,000,000 invested at the beginning of the period turns into $4,306,163. I hope that provides you with a better perspective of what a 7.2 percent compounded annual return actually looks like relative to a specific amount invested.

(Source: Bloomberg, London Share Price Database, and Centre for Research in Finance. Compound average annual returns are In US dollars. The returns are from the following developed and emerging markets: Australia, Austria, Belgium, Brazil, Canada, Chile, China, Colombia, Czech Republic, Denmark, Egypt, Finland, France, Germany, Greece, Hong Kong, Hungary, India, Indonesia, Ireland, Israel, Italy, Japan, Republic of Korea, Malaysia, Mexico, Netherlands, New

Zealand, Norway, Peru, Philippines, Poland, Portugal, Russia, Singapore, South Africa, Spain, Sweden, Switzerland, Taiwan, Thailand, Turkey, United Kingdom, and the United States. Diversification does not eliminate the risk of market loss. Indices are not available for direct investment; therefore, their performance does not reflect the expenses associated with the management of an actual portfolio. Past performance is no guarantee of future results. Investing involves risks, including fluctuating values and potential loss of principal.)

Now, let's take the same exact process and time period with your basket, but before we measure the performance at the end of each year, we take out the top 25 percent performing stocks. Then, we measure its performance just like we did before and come up with a compound annual return over the entire period by averaging each year's return. And what return do we end up with? **-5.4 percent.** Yes, that is a **negative** return (loss) of 5.4 percent, which is certainly not good. And let's put this in perspective using the same future value calculator with a twenty-one-year period at -5.4 percent. After investing $1,000,000, you end up with $311,683. Not so good, especially when compared to the $4,306,163 you had when you had the top 25 percent performers in your basket.

In this time period, it's very clear that when it comes to investing, you don't have a fighting chance if you exclude the top 25 percent stocks in your portfolio. So now comes what I think is one of the most important points in investing that most people don't know; it's where you come to a fork in the road with respect to investment strategy. The conundrum is the following: How do you ensure you have all (or nearly all) of the top performers in your portfolio?

Method 1: Find a system, or a person with a system gleaned from knowledge, experience, and/or analysis, to predict the future consistently over time through decades. The system or person will select the stocks or funds that will be the best performers moving forward, and of course the best time to buy and sell these investments by timing the markets. But wait, we've already established the idea that no one can predict the future. Remember, it may appear that someone has an effective system over a period of time, but one year, five years, or even ten years of data is not necessarily enough to separate skill from luck. That's the reality of the situation, and as they say in Vegas, good luck!

Method 2: (Recommended) Find a way to eliminate as much as possible the risk of trying to predict which stocks will do the best. In other words, ensure as best as possible that you have as many of the top performing stocks in your portfolio because those top performers have more influence over the laggards in the long run. How do you do this? Remember that basket of stocks I referred to earlier that contained just about all of the available stocks in the market? Simply buy the whole basket! Why would you want to do that? To make sure you have all (or very close to it) of those good stocks in the basket. Problem solved, and now you can start looking at other factors in investing that you actually can control to help give you a higher potential return. Yep, that's it. It's a simple, or maybe better stated, an elegant way to give you a higher probability of successful outcomes, but the actual execution and management of the process takes a lot of resources and expertise. But wait, I'm suggesting you buy that whole basket? The basket that includes all of the good performing stocks as well as all the terrible ones and companies that go bankrupt? Yep. Over decades, the overall market indexes have been positive despite all of the failed companies that have been part of those indexes.

So, how do you invest in the global market "basket"?

For starters, invest in low-cost index funds or ETFs. Dimensional Fund Advisors (DFA) and Vanguard do a good job with some differences in cost and the effectiveness of capturing some specific investment factors and avoiding index reconstitution drag, points that would be better discussed with your financial advisor. If you've got somewhere north of about 12,000 global securities in your portfolio, you're doing a good job of capturing the global securities market.

Assuming you now have a way to appropriately diversify and capture the global markets, there's still a question that comes up with older folks who are taking income from their investments and concerned about market risk. There's this investing myth that the older you get, you should automatically get more conservative by, say, holding more bonds or cash. Well, that may be the right thing to do, or it may not.

I've been focusing on stocks, so let's talk about bonds for a moment. In the financial world, we use another term to speak more broadly about this asset class: fixed income. Fixed income is a type of investment security that pays investors fixed interest payments until its maturity date. At maturity, investors are repaid the principal amount they invested. Government and corporate bonds are the most common types of fixed-income products. However, there are fixed income exchange-traded funds and mutual funds available. Treasury bonds and bills, municipal bonds, corporate bonds, and certificates of deposit (CDs) are all examples of fixed-income products.

Fixed income will most likely be an important part of your parents' portfolio, but there are some common misconceptions that are important to understand. One is that fixed income is always safe. Or commonly you might hear, for example, that bonds are safe and provide stable income relative to the stock market. Unfortunately, not all bonds are created equally. Some bonds are actually quite risky. Without getting too technical, there are basically two ways to increase the risk of a bond: increasing the length of maturity (a thirty-year bond vs. a three-month bond) and decreasing the credit quality (junk bond vs. investment grade). Most investors assume the bond allocation in their portfolio is by default, safe. Unfortunately, many investors found out during the 2008 financial crisis that their "safe" bond allocation was actually full of riskier lower credit quality and longer duration bonds; many saw their bonds decrease in value almost as much as their stock portfolio, which is an especially bad situation for investors who are relying on their investments for income. Generally, I recommend investors not take undue risk in their bond portfolio to keep them safe. The most elegant way to do this is to adhere to these principles when investing in bonds: diversify globally, use shorter duration, and use high credit quality. These simple principles will give fixed income portfolios a higher probability that they will be safer.

Another misconception: it is automatically assumed that your investment portfolio should be more conserviative, or have more fixed income vs. stocks, when you get older and retire. This may or may not be the case. The rationale behind the misconception is that as investors get older, they need to be more conservative and reduce the volatility risk of a portfolio. The problem with this approach is that it is only addressing one risk (volatility) and ignoring arguably the most important risk to older people: running out of money before they pass away. If someone retires at age sixty, it's very much within the realm of possibility that they will live for another thirty years, which is a long time to have to rely on an investment portfolio that may be the major source of retirement income. If a portfolio has too much of an allocation to fixed income, it may be destined to have lower returns than a portfolio that does not weigh too heavily on fixed income. The stock portion of a portfolio should be considered the workhorse of the portfolio; it should, if invested correctly, provide higher returns than fixed income over time, thus giving the portfolio a better chance of lasting longer and producing income. Inappropriately weighting a portfolio to fixed income could cause cash flow shortfalls on an annual basis and result in older investors running out of money before they pass away. There are other variables involved that need to be discussed in a comprehensive financial planning environment to come up with the correct investment strategy, but hopefully you get my point. In summary, don't automatically assume a retired person needs to be allocated mostly to fixed income, as this could spell disaster in the long run.

One more common misconception: the yield from bonds is needed to create income and that is the only and best way to create income. The idea is that you create a portfolio full of bonds and the investor, whether an individual or a trust, lives off the interest on the bonds, and this is the best approach. This might be fine in some instances where there is a very defined outcome needed and plenty of assets to cover the need. The problem with this approach is that it totally misses the concept known as "total return." The main benefit and use a total return approach is that the investor uses capital gains in addition to yield from bonds (and stock dividends) to create income. It's a very simple idea in that rather than limiting income source from say, bond yield, you create income from the gains in securities like stocks. We know over time stocks have been a great way to create wealth and have had higher return than bonds, thus the best way to create income via capital gains is via stocks in a total return income-generating strategy. Another benefit of using capital gains as income is that long-term capital gains are taxed at preferential (relative to income tax) long-term capital gains rates if the security has been held longer than one year, which is easily accommodated over time. Simply put, a total return strategy can help an investor's income last longer and be more tax-efficient than other strategies. This concept is so important it has been incorporated into the Uniform Prudent Investor Act and should not only be understood when an investor is constructing an investment portfolio, but also when generating the language of a trust with an attorney.

To wrap things up, there is a lot of "conventional wisdom" in the investment world that is just not supported by academic research. Misconceptions are numerous both from investors and advisors alike so be sure to clarify the foundations and investment philosophy that are most relevant for your parents' circumstances and find a financial advisor with the same philosophy and expertise. With this, hopefully you can help ensure your parents get unconflicted advice from a fiduciary who is able to create a well thought out plan.

Although I've focused on things to look out for in your parents' financial plan and investment strategy it's important to also think about yourself as well. What would happen to you if you suddenly inherited large sums of money? Would you be prepared? Interestingly there's a phenomenon known as "sudden wealth syndrome" (SWS). SWS is a type of distress that affects people who suddenly come into large sums of money. This can cause them to make decisions they might not have otherwise made. Sudden wealth syndrome symptoms include feeling isolated from former friends, feeling guilty about your good fortune, and extreme fear of losing your money.

Sudden wealth syndrome is not an actual psychological diagnosis but was originally coined by therapists who work with patients who have suddenly become wealthy whether it be due to events like inheritance or winning the lottery. The best thing that can be done to help mitigate or avoid SWS is for parents and children to communicate and map things out via family meetings well in advance. Most importantly, if you are receiving large sums of money in a short time frame it's imperative that you have an objective financial advisor to help mitigate the detrimental effects of SWS and provide a steady hand through any emotional difficulties. Most people tend to think that sudden wealth might fix all their problems but in reality it can bring on a whole new set of problems that can cause emotional health issues, family fights, and financial ruin. If you don't think you have the expertise to effectively manage investments for the long term from a technical standpoint, or even if you do, mixing in all of the behavioral issues that come into play just adds on more that can really lead to bad decision making and loss of wealth.

Unfortunately it's not uncommon for people who have experienced sudden wealth to end up penniless in a short amount of time. For example, a married couple won a $13 million lottery ticket and accepted payments of $666,666 per year over a 20-year span in 1990. In 2006 they filed for bankruptcy after living lavish lifestyles in Vegas and enduring a wave of legal expenses resulting from family drama. The couple was later charged with tax evasion and the wife was sentenced to two years in prison and was fined $1.1 million. What could have been an experience-rich and happy life turned into a disaster for this family and there are countless similar stories.

So, if you do inherit large sums of money from your parents don't go out on a spending spree right away. Instead, go through the exercise of creating an intelligent financial plan for yourself and your family. If you do this you'll most likely find you can actually enjoy your newfound wealth for a lifetime rather than a few years and be happy doing it.

Some will tell you that money can't buy happiness. My perspective is: *"Money can't buy happiness, but it's a great down payment."* So, don't blow it.

Life Insurance

Life insurance has its advantages and difficulties.

First the difficulties. If your parents do not have life insurance and they are older and/or have significant medical issues, it is probably cost-prohibitive for them to get it. So, there's a point where if they don't have any, they probably will never get any. The message here for everyone is, if you think you'll have an insurable need, get it earlier in life; your age plays a significant part in the cost of life insurance and you just never know when you'll have a significant medical event that might make you uninsurable.

Someone may be young(er) and very healthy and it seems like there's plenty of time to get it, but then they have a stroke or another significant health event. From then on, their life insurance will most likely be more expensive, even cost-prohibitive, even though they are at an age when they normally could have purchased it cost-effectively.

That is the conundrum with life insurance (and most insurances): it should be purchased when you really don't need it, and that is not much of a motivator. You really have to be forward-thinking with life insurance.

Essentially, there are two flavors of life insurance: permanent and temporary (commonly referred to as term).

Permanent insurance is generally more expensive but designed to last for a lifetime. Term insurance is less expensive and as its name implies, is designed to last for a certain period, like ten or twenty years. Once the term is up, there is no longer any life insurance paid to the beneficiaries. So let's say your sixty-year-old father tells you he's got plenty of life insurance. That's good and you move on. But what you don't know is that he has ten more years on a twenty-year policy he bought ten years ago. When he passes away at age seventy-one, guess what? No life insurance for any surviving beneficiaries. This is a surprise that is not worth having. Thus, permanent life insurance is better if you have an expectation of a benefit regardless of when someone passes away, but it is generally more expensive and often cost-prohibitive.

Another benefit of permanent life insurance is that the policies usually have significantly more cash value in the policy that can be used while your parent is living as a source for unexpected cash flow needs. Term insurance will have very little if any cash value in the policy, so it is not a good source for cash if needed while living.

Those are the general themes of life insurance. In reality, they are much more complicated and there are many hybrid flavors of insurance within themselves and also combinations with other products. Hopefully, your parents have worked with a reputable licensed insurance agent and made their decisions with their eyes wide open—but over time the details can get foggy. If you want to get a handle on your parents' life insurance contract, contact the company that holds the policy and ask for an in-force illustration. This is a fairly detailed report that can be reviewed by your parents, yourself, and anyone else of interest; it should clear up any questions or at least get the ball rolling in the right direction.

One of the best things life insurance can do is to provide liquidity for the beneficiaries to balance out asset distribution upon the death of the policy owner. For instance, let's say parents who have passed away left their home to their two children. If one of the children wants his portion of the home in cash now and the other child does not have enough money to buy him out, it can cause a lot of problems. Parents with foresight can alleviate this issue by having enough life insurance so either child has enough liquidity to buy out the other. This is a very simple scenario, but it can be very complicated and cause a tremendous amount of anxiety and discord within a family if things aren't thought out. Add in more siblings and multiple properties and you can see that proper planning with life insurance can help the beneficiaries (including you) significantly.

Also, one of the most prominent rationales for purchasing life insurance of course is to pay for estate taxes. But, depending on your parents' circumstances, they may or may not have any estate tax due. Again, proper planning and forecasting should help clarify the issue.

Long-Term Care Insurance

Long-term care (LTC) insurance is not an insignificant cost, but it could potentially help your parents avoid financial ruin should they need care for longer periods.

Before we talk about LTC insurance, let's clarify what it is. It's different from disability insurance in that disability insurance replaces a portion of your income lost due to an inability to perform your job whereas LTC insurance pays for a portion or all of the costs of caregiving needed due to physical or cognitive disability which can last for several months or several decades. Aging parents will most likely need long-term care when they have an ongoing health condition or disability that is relatively serious. As with most of the issues that arise with aging parents, the need for LTC can come very quickly so it's good to have everything lined up prior to a critical event occurring. For example, everything could be fine and then one day your parent has a stroke and in an instance your lives change and they'll need LTC immediately. Having said that, the usual path is a gradual decline as your parents get older. An example would be a disability they've had for awhile just keeps getting worse and they are no longer able to function on their own.

Help with everyday activities, which are also called "activities of daily living" or ADL's are the categories that the industry tests for benefits and the most prevalent type are activities related to personal care. The specific activities include eating, using the toilet, grooming, bathing, dressing, and also moving around - for example getting up from a chair or into bed. Community services such as transportation and meals are also categorized as LTC and they are sometimes provided at a cost or for free.

A LTC policy holder is able to start receiving benefits if they are unable to perform two of the ADL's listed above or they are diagnosed to be mentally incompetent. Documentation for any of these conditions must come from a primary physician or a specialist and must be submitted to the insurance company in order to begin receiving benefits. Once the physician's diagnosis has been submitted, the insurance company may discuss the case with the physician to clarify any details but it's generally rare for an insurance company to repudiate a formal diagnosis.

Many LTC insurance policies also typically have waiting periods, benefit periods, and other factors that need to be understood. The bottom line is this: it's important to speak with a professional who understands all the nuances of LTC insurance policies both for purchase and to prepare for the time when it's needed.

The LTC insurance industry has been changing in recent years and they are transitioning from specific LTC policies to life insurance policies with LTC riders attached to them. One of the reasons for doing this is that many of the older LTC policies, which your parent may very well have, did not have a premium guarantee which means that many LTC insurance premiums have been getting more expensive for policyholders as they get older. Your parent's might have thought their premiums were going to remain at the level when the policy was originally purchased only to find out they are having to pay more for coverage as they get older. This can be a big issue for the elderly on a fixed budget. Another issue with many of the older policies is that they were "use it or lose it" meaning that someone could have paid their LTC insurance premiums for decades and never actually needed the benefits. In this case, all of the premiums paid are lost to the family.

Newer policies that are structured as life insurance policies with LTC riders resolve these issues. The good policies will have a "level premium" meaning that the premium will never go up and if LTC benefits are never needed, all of the premiums will be returned either to the surviving spouse or the estate in the form of life insurance depending on how much of the LTC benefits were actually used and whether or not it is a first or second-to-die policy.

If you find that your parent's circumstances have changed and the premium is too high or you don't think they need as much of a benefit as originally contracted then it should be fairly simple to contact the insurance company and reduce the coverage within the existing contract. Conversely if you believe your parents need increased coverage, they will have to supplement their current coverage with a new LTC policy which means they will have to go through underwriting again. The older a person becomes, the higher the probability that they may be denied a new policy due to health issues and almost a certainty that premiums will be higher (because they are older) so never cancel an existing policy with the expectation of replacing or supplementing insurance until everything has been finalized and approved in writing. Also, many older policies did not provide benefits if the policy holder was at home, they only provided for benefits when a policyholder was admitted into a facility. Everyone involved realized this was not an ideal outcome as many elderly want to stay at home in their declining years and it can be more cost efficient for the family and the insurance company as well. With that, most newer LTC policies provide equal coverage for in-home and facility care benefits but be sure to have your parents check their policies for this nuance.

I had fortunately done my research and knew my parent's older LTC policy did not pay for in-home care. It's essential that you review these policies prior to the time you need them so you understand their benefit amounts, qualifying criteria, waiting periods, and benefit periods. For many parents, their ideal scenario is that they want to stay at home in their decline through death. But what if that scenario would potentially exhaust all the financial resources of the estate, leaving the surviving parent with no or little recourse financially in the future? Would that be something you want your parents to experience? Would that be something they want to experience? Perhaps it's a personal choice, but generally speaking, the responsible course of action is to help your parents fulfill their wishes without being financially irresponsible.

Document Consolidation

As I mentioned previously, my father had his "Toes Up File," a manilla folder where he had all his important documents filed for easy access when he passed away. His wry sense of humor notwithstanding, it's important that your parents have a well-thought-out approach to making the administrative issues as easy as possible for their spouses and/or children.

There are countless cases of spouses and children who are all of a sudden thrown into scenarios where they have to help a family member but have no idea where the necessary documents are. For that matter, most of us might have a hard time finding our own personal documents when needed.

Imagine if there was a medical emergency with your only surviving parent and you had no idea what her health coverage was, who the primary doctor was, and where to go to get money if needed. What happens if your mom with Alzheimer's needs long-term care and can't remember if she even has long-term care insurance? What if she passes away and you need to contact her life insurance company and look at the house deed? And the list goes on.

Hopefully, you can understand what a nightmare it would be for you if your parents did not have things organized for you or whoever will be stepping in to help. Wanting to help but not being able to can be the worst frustration. Not having everything organized is simply a huge time suck—when at your stage of life, time is likely one of your most precious resources. You can see it's important to discuss these issues with your parents and perhaps roll up your sleeves to help them get on the right path if they just can't get around to it.

Getting everything together in one place is a great start. Where to keep everything is another issue. Putting the file in a desk drawer worked for my dad, luckily. Unfortunately the desk drawer is not necessarily the most secure place. You could have them get a safe and put everything in it, but there are still a few issues to consider. For instance, a safe is good unless you don't know or can't find the key or combination. I'm sure it would be extremely frustrating to be staring at a safe that holds everything you need—but you can't get into it.

Here's a story worth hearing. In the 2000s, there were several significant fires that tore through neighborhoods in San Diego fueled by dry shrubs and hot, dry winds blowing from the desert known as Santa Ana winds. Many homes were destroyed and families displaced and the air was thick with soot and ash. There is no real bright side to these tragedies other than beautiful sunsets and the acceptance of death and rebirth with the landscape and displaced lives. After the fires were under control, families that had their homes burned down began the process of rebuilding. For that to begin, they needed to get their documents together—like homeowners insurance and other paperwork to help them continue their lives. Being a financial advisor in the area, I knew many other professionals, like bankers, attorneys, private fiduciaries, etc. One fairly common story I heard was that people opened their safes—where they stored all their important documents and sometimes significant amounts of cash—and found nothing but charred and burned paper. Ouch. Even people who thought their safes were "fireproof" did not fully grasp the amount of heat that would be generated by the fires.

So how do you avoid losing access to important documents, whether it be to fire, flood, or some other disaster? The answer is simple: scan all your documents and upload them to a secure cloud filing system. Easier yet, have the originating company send you the documents electronically (and securely) and just upload them from your computer. There are many options out there for you, including Dropbox, Google Drive, etc.

My investment firm, WorthPointe, uses a financial planning tool for our clients called eMoney. Along with their own personal financial portal that consolidates all their net asset details, it serves as a digital vault that allows them to upload any important documents, like life insurance policies, trusts, POAs, house deeds, etc.

While it's not a bad idea to have hard copy documents organized in one place at your parents' home, I highly recommend you have them organized and available in a secure digital vault as well. A further benefit to this type of storage is that you can access these documents from anywhere at any time—even if you don't live with or near your parents.

Splitting Assets Among Multiple Beneficiaries

One area of investing that often isn't given much thought is how assets are going to be equally divided among beneficiaries, assuming this is the goal of your parents. As a financial advisor, I can't tell you how many times I've come across parents with real estate they like and thus don't want to sell, but want to pass on to their kids. There are a whole lot of issues that need to be considered here.

Let's take a simple example I've already used, of parents with two children who own one home they want to pass on to them. It's a noble pursuit but comes with some issues. How do you split the home between the two children? Chainsaw? (There's always one in the crowd.) Technically, that would work, but of course you won't be winning any genius awards.

When your parents pass away, you're effectively a business partner with your sibling(s) in a home. Might work. For awhile. There generally comes a time, though, when one of the siblings needs cash—tuition for the kids, business opportunity, big vacation, any number of scenarios come to mind. Then what do you do? While there are some options, they all present challenges. What's my point? An easy way to divide assets to multiple beneficiaries is to actually have assets that are practically dividable, like liquid investment accounts (stocks, bonds, cash).

When a family home is in play, there's a pretty good chance its value has appreciated significantly over the decades. I think this issue causes a lot more stress and forced financial decisions to the detriment of those involved and is not discussed as much as it should be. For instance, if a sibling wants to buy another's share of an inherited home, there's a high probability he or she won't have enough cash sitting around to do that. One way to resolve this issue—already mentioned but worth repeating—is for parents to provide for enough life insurance to provide siblings with liquid assets (cash) to facilitate a buyout.

Trust/Wills/DPOAs

A will or testament is a legal document by which a person, the testator, expresses their wishes as to how their property is to be distributed at death, and names one or more persons, the executor(s), to manage the estate until its final distribution. Different states have different laws for the creation of wills, so it is highly recommended that an estate planning attorney in the state of your parents' residence is used to draft the document. If the document was created years ago, it is highly recommended to have it reviewed and updated.

Your parents might have everything set up nicely with regard to wills and how things will be disbursed to beneficiaries, so everything is all set and you are good to go, right? Nope. There are additional things you must put in place to ensure you can actually help your parents—powers of attorney.

A power of attorney (POA) is a document that allows you to appoint a person or organization to manage your affairs if you become unable to do so. However, all POAs are not created equal. Each type gives your attorney-in-fact (the person who will be making decisions on your behalf) a different level of control. In relation to your parents, you may be selected to be their "attorney-in-fact" for issues that need to be resolved should they not be able to do so on their own.

Let's say your mom is living at home and has to go to the hospital for a short stay for the flu. You decide to stop by the house and check on her mail and bills and notice she received a disconnect notice on her phone because the bill is overdue and needs to be paid as soon as possible. You think to yourself, "Okay, I've got this. I know my mom has all her documents together and she's named me as the person to help, so I'll just call the phone company and get this squared away."

You call the phone company and they ask for your account number, phone number, last four digits of your Social Security number, and PIN. You have a mental pause and think, "Well, they're asking for *my* information, but I'm calling for my mom, and the robo receptionist is not smart enough to ask me that." You finally get to a live person who asks you to confirm your information; you tell her you're calling for your mom, so she asks you for all your mom's information—and you probably don't have her Social Security number or PIN handy. You start to get frustrated because this is taking too much time.

Let's say you finally wade through the bureaucratic conversation and she then says, "Great, how may I help you?" You reply that you want to see what's going on with your mom's account because she's in the hospital. And the response is, "I'm sorry sir (or ma'am), you are not authorized as someone who I can share information with. Can you get your mom on the line?" And so the conversation goes, off the path into thickets your best verbal machete will not be able to hack through.

As this example illustrates, it's not just a matter of having your parents figure out who they want handling their affairs if they are not able to. You need to have a notarized Durable Power of Attorney (DPOA) on file for any company or institution they might be contractually or legally affiliated with. This includes, but is not limited to, insurance companies, banks, investment firms, and utility companies.

Once your DPOAs are received by these companies, the conversation will be much different. "Yes sir (or ma'am), I see you as an authorized agent so we can take care of this now."

I can't emphasize how important it is to get DPOAs in place **prior** to any situations arising so you can best be of help during these times. It will also reduce your stress significantly and improve your time efficiency in dealing with these issues, thus making the whole effort of helping your parents more feasible.

Healthcare Directives & Power of Attorney

A healthcare POA, also called an advance health care directive in some states, grants someone authority to make medical decisions for your parent if he or she is unconscious, mentally incompetent, or otherwise unable to make decisions on his or her own. While not the same thing as a living will, many states allow you to include your preference about being kept on life support. There are some states that will allow you to combine the wishes usually if they are documented in a living will, into your healthcare POA or advanced healthcare directive.

It's really important for you and/or responsible parties to understand your parent's wishes regarding end-of-life scenarios. If you can't remember the particulars, at the very least, ensure you have the documents readily available to guide you when needed. It also makes sense to ensure the hospital staff and caregivers have a copy of these documents on file. You definitely don't want to be at a loss when people are turning to you for a decision that may affect end-of-life treatment.

There are two main forms of Advanced Care Planning (ACP) documents: advance directives (ADs) and physician orders for life sustaining treatment (POLST). ADs are legal documents that can be completed at any time in life to guide future care and/or appoint someone else as a decision-maker. ADs must be completed by the person they cover and require either a witness or notary, depending on the state. POLST forms are a little different. They are physician orders for end-of-life care designed to be transferred among healthcare institutions. POLST is an approach to improving end-of-life care, encouraging providers to speak with patients and create specific medical orders to be honored by healthcare workers during a medical crisis. The POLST form is always signed by a medical professional, and depending on the state, the patient. A pragmatic test for initiating a POLST can be if the clinician would not be surprised if the patient were to die within one year. One difference between a POLST form and an advanced care directive is that the POLST form is designed to be actionable throughout an entire community. It is immediately recognizable and can be used by doctors and first responders (including paramedics, fire departments, police, emergency rooms, hospitals, and nursing homes). They are printed on bright pink paper and should be placed on the client's refrigerator.

Do Not Resuscitate

Do Not Resuscitate (DNR) is a legal order that indicates a person does not want to receive resuscitation efforts and possibly other medical efforts. It's really important that a DNR order is readily available and on file with your parents' doctor. I was just speaking with a doctor who sees many patients who in normal circumstances have no chance of survival without medical intervention, but are left stagnating in beds hooked up to machines. In several instances, these were homeless patients with no identifiable next-of-kin, so the medical staff was unable to do anything other than "treat" them. Some institutions have entire rooms set up with patients in similar states.

There are several ways a DNR can be put in place:

1. Use a form provided by a doctor

2. Write your wishes down yourself

3. Call your health department or state department on aging to get a form

Generally, if your parents' doctor has already written a DNR order at his or her request, your family may not override it. You may have been named by your parents as a healthcare agent to speak for them. If so, a legal guardian can agree to a DNR order for someone.

If you think these issues might be nice to know but don't have significant repercussions, here's a story for you. A recent incident in which "Do Not Resuscitate" was tattooed on an unconscious patient's chest caused a significant amount of confusion with the hospital staff as there really was no precedence and they had to discuss it with their ethics consultants. After making a decision and then reversing the decision they finally decided to honor the tattoo. A very interesting situation and it highlights the fact that clarity of wishes is very important.

Probate vs. Trust

An important point to consider is that even if there is a will, its validity, if questioned, will have to be decided by a probate court. Probate court is a specialized type of court that deals with the property and debts of a person who has died. The basic role of the probate court judge is to ensure the deceased person's creditors are paid, all potential beneficiaries and heirs are notified and aware of the proceedings, and any remaining assets are distributed to the proper beneficiaries. Probate is a legal procedure where a court oversees the distribution of property of a person who has died. Many states have a specialized probate court. In some states it is called by other names, such as Surrogate's Court, Orphan's Court, or Chancery Court. The court appoints someone to take control of the deceased person's assets, ensure all debts are properly paid, and distribute the remaining property to the proper beneficiaries.

The worst-case scenario is having a parent die without a will, so everything goes to probate court for a judge to decide. In this case, the state determines where assets will go as opposed to your parents having a say in it. When a person dies without a will, the property is distributed to the deceased person's next of kin, as determined by the state's probate law. This part of the probate law is known as the law of intestate succession. It outlines the order in which the next of kin inherit. A surviving spouse gets a share of the decedent's property. The law further breaks down the order in which grandchildren, siblings, parents, aunts, and uncles inherit. The details vary from state to state. In a sense, the law of intestate succession can be considered to be the "will" the state makes for you if you don't make your own.

I recently heard a story about a husband and father of three (we'll call him Lance) in his early forties who had a financial firm that was doing very well and afforded the family a great lifestyle. He was skiing, got into an accident, and was killed. Unfortunately, his company was really just a company of one and the real value of the firm was Lance and his unique knowledge and skill set. Furthermore, he died without a will and did not have life insurance and his company instantly had no value. Needless to say, his surviving spouse and children were in a terrible situation immediately and unrecoverably for the foreseeable future. They are probably out there, but I can't think of a much worse scenario you might hear—and this leads to the idea of ensuring your documents and planning are in place.

Even if your deceased parents had a will, there may be a need for a probate process if there are any disagreements from creditors or siblings as to the validity of the process. The costs of probate include, among other things, court filing fees, costs for publishing notices in newspapers, and attorney's and executor's fees can add up. If the estate is complex, there may also be fees for an accountant. Fees for a probate attorney may be based on an hourly rate, a percentage of the value of the estate, or a combination of the two.

The probate process can take months, or even years, to complete. For an average modest estate, it can take from six months to two years. The longer it takes, the more it costs. If any heirs contest a will, things get more time-consuming and expensive.

Probate also makes the deceased person's financial situation a matter of public record. This includes the nature and extent of the assets, the person's debts, and who will get the assets.

Many people seek ways to either avoid probate, or to minimize the amount of their property that will be subject to probate. This can be accomplished by restructuring the manner in which property is held and holding assets in a living trust.

All Trusts Are Not Created Equal

Before I get too deep into talking about trusts, it's worth sorting out some overall basics.

In the context of this book, i.e., helping your aging parents, your parents would be the grantor (also called a trustor) and you would most likely be a beneficiary.

Trusts can be created for many reasons that include

- Protecting the beneficiaries from creditors

- Protecting young beneficiaries who are young or not financially astute

- Protecting the disabled and their benefits

- Avoiding probate court

- Reducing estate taxes

- Fulfilling the needs of family including future generations generations

Generally, a trust can either be revocable or irrevocable, and the difference between the two is readily apparent in the terminology. A revocable trust is a trust that can be revoked or altered by the grantor. Assets in a revocable trust are usually considered to be part of the grantor's estate and thus used in the calculation of the estate for estate tax purposes. An irrevocable trust, on the other hand, is not usually revocable nor can the terms be amended or modified without the permission of the beneficiaries. The assets held within an irrevocable trust would typically not be counted as being part of your parents' estate for estate tax purposes when they pass away.

To be clear, there are many types of trusts and some terms that refer to the same type of trust, so it can get a little confusing. Here is a list of some of the types and terms you will typically find when working with your parents:

- Charitable Remainder Trust—This is an irrevocable trust that can create an income for the grantors while they are living and then the remaining value of the assets are gifted to a charity.

- Revocable Living Trust—This type of trust is created to transfer property from an individual's name (person) to the trust. The grantor stays in control of the trust during their lifetime.

- Family Trust—This is just another name for a Revocable Living Trust.

- Generation Skipping Trust—This type of trust skips a generation when passing assets- typically to grandchildren instead of children.

- Bypass Trust (also called Credit Shelter Trust)— Spouses who are planning their estate and financial affairs typically use this trust for planning and is generally concerned with the taxation of the assets.

- Survivor's Trust—Placing assets from a deceased spouse into a trust for the remaining spouse is usually carried out by means of a survivor's trust. There are usually no restrictions on how the surviving spouse can use the assets in this trust.

- QTIP Trust—This is a trust created for a remaining spouses income needs but the remaining assets are eventually passed onto children.

- Irrevocable Life Insurance Trust (ILIT)—This is where a life insurance policy is put into and owned by a trust, as opposed to being owned by an individual, to avoid estate taxes on life insurance payouts.

Living Trust

One of the most convenient and common ways to avoid any of the above mentioned issues is to create a living trust, also referred to as a family or revocable trust. A living trust is a legal document wherein your assets are placed into a trust for your benefit while you are living. When you pass away the assets are then transferred to designated beneficiaries. This is an example of a trust that is revocable, which means at any time the trustees can revoke the trust or change it. This differs greatly from an irrevocable trust, which as the name implies, is not revocable and has more stringent conditions placed on it.

It's a great planning tool to have a living trust in place. It really adds clarity and efficiency throughout the lives of the trustees and after their passing as they lay out what assets are given to which beneficiaries, how, and when.

A very important point to remember is that just because a trust is created does not mean it is funded. What does this mean? Let's take an example and say your parents own a home and an investment account and they create a living trust for their assets and all of the benefits that come with a trust. So, they create the trust with an estate planning attorney and they are done, correct? No. They must, in this case, change ownership of their home and investment account from their person(s) (individually or jointly) to the trust. And yes, it is actually a change in ownership and titling. So for the home, it would go from being owned by say Bob and Mary Smith to The Bob and Mary Smith Living Trust. Think of the trust as an empty bucket when created. You then must fill the bucket with the family assets and you can only do that by re-titling the assets as being owned by the trust. I bring this up as there have been many instances where trusts were created and the trustees (parents) never got around to retitling the assets to the trust, so in effect the trust was just a useless piece of paper and their estate had to go through probate. As you go through things with your parents, pay particular attention to this issue.

Asset Structure

I recently wrote an article on elegance for life. Most people at some point would like to experience a simplistic elegance in their life and one of the most important ways to help you do this is to imbue your financial ecosystem with simplicity and elegance as well. It's well worth thinking about asset structure when thinking about passing your assets to family members and simplicity or elegance will help immensely. Unfortunately, people sometimes want to retain the complicated and time-consuming investment schemes and structures that have gotten them where they are, such as:

- Owning a business

- Owning real estate

- Maintaining multiple accounts at multiple institutions

Anyone who owns or has owned real estate or a business knows how time-consuming, costly, and complicated they can be to manage effectively; it's self-evident. But what most people don't fully grasp are the liquidity complications of these investments. Liquidity refers to the ability to quickly convert your investment to cash. In retirement, you should be able to get your hard-earned cash when you want it, but with real estate and business ownership, unfortunately that may not be possible. This is referred to as liquidity risk. Furthermore, these types of assets are sometimes difficult to pass on to children with differing aptitudes and needs. Of course they can be passed on effectively, but usually require yet again more complicated and costly legal structures and administration to do so.

The main point here is it will be worth it for your parents to think about the ease of splitting up assets in their configuration and see if there is anything that can be done to make the process more efficient when the time comes.

I previously touched on a situation where parents own an investment property and want to leave it to three children. One child might want to live there, another might want to rent it out for income, and another might want to sell it and use the cash for something else. So although the parents thought they were doing a lot of good leaving their three children an investment property, they were most likely ensuring none of them were entirely happy and potentially causing future conflict between them.

It's also difficult when parents have a family business and want to give their children equal ownership in the business when they pass away. For sure one or more of the children will not be interested or may not have the capability to run the business effectively so that usually ends up being a mess. If you are in this situation it's important that you are able to effectively communicate with your parent/owner your goals and interests as they relate to the business. There are some very good strategies to plan for passing businesses onto children and allowing for a benefit both for children that do and do not want to be involved but they will take some time, commitment, and effort to be properly put in place well prior to an owner's passing.

If on the other hand, parents had left these three children a fully liquid investment account that could easily be split among them, a lot of issues could be solved and the parents could maximize the perceived benefit. Issues such as step-up-in basis might be reasons not to do this prior to death, so again, proper planning and communication are paramount.

Web Access & Passwords

With today's advances in technology, just about any account your parents have, whether it be for utilities or financial institutions, is going to have a website requiring a username and password. People are notorious for forgetting usernames and passwords. Also, websites are always asking users to update their passwords. You've seen the messages before: "Password must be at least twelve characters in length with at least three numbers and one special character. They must be all prime numbers whose square root is less than the number pi and if multiplied represent the sides of an isosceles triangle…"

In addition, there are often multi-factor sign-on processes that may require a passcode, answers to personal questions, and responses to text or email messages. If you plan on helping your parents it's essential that you have an effective method of accessing these websites and passwords from anywhere. You might be challenged just keeping up with your own; now imagine doing the same thing for someone else.

I've found the best way to do this is by using a passcode keeper. There are plenty out there to choose from, but essentially they require you to only remember one passcode for the password vault and then you have access to all the information you need. I happen to use Keeper Password Manager. Among other utilities, it automatically generates and stores strong passwords along with usernames, URLs, and notes. It's helped me personally for my passwords and was very helpful with my mother when I started paying her bills through the time of settling the estate.

In practice, she gave me the usernames/passwords for her websites and I was able to generate a separate folder for her within Keeper to keep track of them. Really, though, I ended up setting most of this up, as she mostly did all of her account management with paper statements and physical checks and didn't do much on the internet. From there, I was able to manage everything for her, regardless of where I was. Furthermore, when I decided to hire a bill paying service for her, I was able to share select records with them directly through the application so they could access and pay all of her accounts online. So, I can't emphasize enough how important it was for me to have a password manager. Remember, you might need a POA at the company on file to set everything up and it's important to do this prior to someone becoming totally incapacitated—as you'll be too busy and might not be able to get everything done.

When A Parent Did Not Leave a Will

A parent is said to have died "intestate" when they did not leave a will. Children will usually have rights of inheritance under certain circumstances if their parent dies without a will, especially in states that are not community property states. In community property states, a surviving spouse is usually entitled to a deceased spouse's half of the estate—and the half she already owns. However, a surviving spouse may not be entitled to the same amount in states that are common-law states. In common-law states it is not unusual for the surviving spouse to get at least one half of the estate if for example they had one child. However, if the deceased parent did not make a will and had more than one child, it is common for the surviving spouse to receive one-third of the estate, with the other two-thirds typically passing to her children in equal shares.

Probate

Simply put, a parent's estate may be probated whether or not there is a will. Probate courts help divide property according to a will or the inheritance laws of a particular state. If a parent left a will, and the will was admitted to probate court, children typically have the right to an accounting of their parent's assets from the executor of the estate.

Will Contests

Children also have a right to contest a parent's will if they have valid legal grounds. For example, if a child was left out of a will and believes the document is invalid because her parent was controlled by another person while making it—or lacked the capacity to understand what she was doing while making it—the child may contest the will in probate court. If the probate court is satisfied with the child's testimony, it may grant an appropriate share of the parent's estate to the child.

Sometimes, children are prone to suing their siblings and there are a few circumstances that increase the probability of this occurring:

- Poor communication amongst family members

- A will was changed when a parent had diminished mental capacity

- Unequal distributions to children

- Disinheritance of a child

- One child provides care for a parent and thinks they should have presumes a higher portion of distributions

The best thing you can do to avoid a lot of these issues is to impress upon your parents the importance of communication with all children. Most parents know which kids are responsible—the one(s) they'd trust with their affairs—but many will also be blinded by love, guilt, or other emotional issues and not be able to take a practical stance.

In my opinion, the best scenario is for your parents to sit down with their financial advisor and estate planning attorney so they can thoughtfully and intelligently work out these issues and put them on paper. This could then be followed up with a family meeting mediated by the financial advisor and/or estate planning attorney. There is a risk that the communication of parental wishes to children while the parents are still living might bring forth some discontent for the children who did not agree with what is going on, but the truth is better than denial, and at the end of the day, the parents will most likely have the full authority and right to be making the decisions as they see fit.

If your family relations are strained so much that it would be a huge hurdle to even communicate these issues, it's certainly understandable that putting one child in charge as trustee would be at the very least problematic. In these instances, and even if there is no contention, it might make sense for your parents to transfer any administration of their estate to a third party such as a private fiduciary or corporate trustee. I'll discuss family meetings, private fiduciaries, and corporate trustees in more detail later.

Decline

I was in my mid-forties by the time my father's dementia started becoming apparent. Initially, it was kind of a joke that he couldn't remember things, and then I noticed he was hesitant to go out and do the things he used to enjoy. Dementia patients start developing tricks and crutches to hide the full extent of their disease—like using notes on a desk or in a book to help them remember. When my father had a hard time being able to write and do simple arithmetic, we had to step in and make changes. My mom started doing the bills and we got a caregiver to help around the house, because at this point my mom had been partially disabled for years due to a stroke. All of a sudden, things started accelerating; it was the point where circumstances can quickly get ahead of you.

Very soon, we realized my father needed twenty-four-hour care. Since my mom was disabled, we either had to hire caretakers to come into the home or have him moved to a living facility with a cognitive care unit. (Realize that parents with a cognitive disease such as dementia and Alzheimers present a unique challenge. You most likely want to ensure any care that's provided is by someone with expertise in this area.)

Ultimately, the decision was made to admit my father into the cognitive care facility at a retirement home. Thankfully, his LTC policy covered 100 percent of the cost of care. This allowed my disabled mother to stay in the house with part-time caretakers and not break the bank. Also thankfully, the facility was two blocks from our family house, so we were able to bring my father back home some days in the earlier stages of his decline, and we were able to visit him frequently in the latter stages.

In my opinion, cognitive disorders are easier on the patient than they are on the family and friends surrounding them. That's not to take away from the difficult mental decline and physical pain one must experience throughout this disease. I can more than imagine this, as I've seen it up close and personal. Every patient has slightly different emotional tendencies as they progress through cognitive disorders. Some who have been kind all their lives will become very different people—agitated, angry, and combative. This is a very tough thing to experience as a son or daughter, as the person you've known for years, the parent who was a rock and guided you through life, becomes a person you don't really recognize.

In my father's case, as his dementia worsened he just became more of a happy kid. To clarify, it was as if he was a young boy who was happy and naive, and felt and exuded a pure innocent love for me as if I was a friend or father. It was a real role reversal that was very touching, but at times created an upwelling of sadness I could not repress. That's what I mean by the idea that it can be much more difficult for family and friends than for the person who actually has the disease. There were moments when my dad would look me in the eye, hold my hand, and say something simple like, "Thank you for coming. I missed you." He was innocently serene and pure, but I felt my heart was being crushed.

In these moments, you'll realize what I spoke about earlier—having the tools and resources to deal with your emotional and spiritual foundation—becomes essential. After a visit like this, if you are not prepared, or even if you are, you will most likely be emotionally drained and it does not get any better. You essentially have two choices: avoidance or acceptance. Many will avoid. You can't handle it. It's too distressing and you need to keep your act together for your work, your family, and your health. We get it. We're not judging. It's not easy. In my case, I would meditate prior to these visits, focusing on Metta meditation (loving kindness) to build up my heart and emotional strength and get the right perspective. I viewed this time with my father as a life work of love, effort, and honor. I wanted all that to flow from me to my father, so I had to recharge my emotional batteries prior to my visits. I did not want to show up and have him see or feel my sadness or distress, as I'm sure that wouldn't have helped him.

Ultimately, a cognitive disorder like dementia is a disease not only of the mind, but the body. Most people's impressions of these types of cognitive diseases is an understanding that the mind will degrade but the body can remain healthy. Well, that is true up to a certain point. You have to remember that the mind is also intimately intertwined with all the regulatory processes in the body that keep you healthy. When the mind is not able to send the right signals to the body, the degradation of the body accelerates toward death.

One day I visited my father and was shocked at the downturn he had taken. He had withered up in his bed, had labored breathing, and his gray eyes stared up at the ceiling. A thought came to mind that I quickly repressed, that he looked as if death had taken him but he was still breathing. I went to sit beside him and he became a little agitated, so I just held his hand, spoke to him, and did some Metta meditation. He calmed down and I just thought how much I loved him and how I wished we could go back to the Austrian Alps and go hiking together.

Knowing I could not hold on to that hope, I then wished he would pass as peacefully and quickly as possible, but I did not think it would happen soon. Little did I know that he was in his final days.

A decline in your parents' health can go through cycles and at times can settle into a long-term affair followed by a sudden ending of life. Regardless of your experience, there are some important things to consider and accomplish during this phase.

Medication

There's a high probability your aging parent will be on at least one medication, if not many of them. In my father's case, he was not on any medication. In my mother's case, she was on multiple medications due to her stroke, including pain relievers, blood thinners, antidepressants, and several others. My personal belief is that we are generally over-prescribed in the modern era. It's really a weird thing when they advertise a medication on TV and provide a long list of potential side effects—". . .may cause insomnia, permanent liver damage, and death. . ."—while the actors are smiling and picking flowers in a field. Having said that, it's hard to argue against someone taking medications who had something like a stroke and may be unable to function otherwise because of pain, etc.

The best advice I can give is to know exactly what medications your parents are taking, how long they have been taking them, and what the side effects are, and ensure you are at least somewhat familiar with the interactions between them. It's important to look at both prescribed and over-the-counter drugs, including non-oral medications such as injections, inhalers, ointments, and drops, as well as medications only taken occasionally.

In 2017, my mom had gotten to the point where she could with effort get herself from the bedroom to the kitchen, but most of the time she was using an indoor scooter. She still drove herself to the YMCA pool every week to participate in a water exercise program, which was great physically and emotionally since she had a lot of friends there. She at least had some semblance of independence. At this point, I was living in Austin, Texas, while my mom was still in Coronado, so it was no longer a twenty-minute drive to get to her house. One day, I received a phone call that she was admitted into the emergency room. She was sent back home, but readmitted in January and initially diagnosed with pneumonia. The result of her symptoms was that she was no longer able to get around, even in the house, as her energy level was really low. This was exacerbated by the fact that she had her teeth pulled for dentures, was on a difficult liquid diet for some time, and had lost some weight. The bottom line was that my mom now needed help with most aspects of daily living twenty-four hours a day.

It was a great relief that my sister had come to town at this point, helping to coordinate things and I was able to fly in the next day. One day when my sister was with my mom in her hospital room, she told me that mom started hallucinating heavily and had become very agitated. This was day two of my mothers' stay in the hospital. I went to see what was going on and was shocked at what I saw. My mom was talking in tongues, grasping at ghosts, shaking, anxious, and was having trouble breathing; I thought this was it. I was, to say the least, very worried and shocked at her condition. And then, here's the kicker, the hospital staff came into the room and said she was ready to be discharged. What? Did I hear that correctly? I was shocked. What could they possibly be thinking saying my mom was ready to be discharged when she was obviously in extreme physiological stress? But they wouldn't budge and looking at the administrator I just got a really weird vibe. My sister and I were beside ourselves and needed to start moving up the hospital administration food chain. I brought in the floor manager and a case manager and they essentially told me the same thing—she needed to be discharged due to some legal/regulatory/administration issues that I sensed were there but could not be fully grasped by my stressed mind.

At that point I decided to go to the top. I called the CEO's office, which was onsite, to speak with her. I was informed that she was not in the office, but she would be given a message to call me. I left that morning and gathered my thoughts at the nearby family house. After not hearing anything for a couple hours, I decided to go on a mission at the hospital and not leave until I spoke with the CEO. It was a Friday afternoon and the pressure was on, as I did not want things to roll into the weekend.

For whatever reason, I walked into the hospital via a side door, and in my peripheral vision, I saw a group of hospital staffers gathered, eating. In a microsecond, my mind came to the conclusion that it was a Friday staff gathering and the CEO would be there. I walked into the courtyard, and sure enough, the CEO was serving food to some of the staff. I walked up to her, apologized for breaking up her Friday party and told her I needed to speak with her about my mom. I was not angry with her nor did I approach her aggressively, which I knew would have not helped my cause. She looked at me with a smile on her face and said, "Okay, let's go up to my office now."

We went up there together; I called my sister and she met us. I laid out the facts of my mom's situation and was expecting some resistance. She looked at me with compassion and a smile and said, "We need to take care of this." With that, she called up the case manager, another administrative person I had identified, and got her input. At the end of the meeting, she declared my mom would not be discharged and needed to be further evaluated. I had such a rush of relief, I couldn't fight the tears that came to my eyes. I guess the shock of seeing my mom in that state and the challenges we were facing just got to me. I was too busy to completely ascertain what the issues were and why they wanted to discharge her, so I can't accuse the hospital of trying to push an early discharge when it wasn't called for. Having said that, remember this happened on day two, which is relevant.

It turns out there is a connection between hospital stay duration and coverage for skilled care. To begin, you must understand there's a difference between a skilled nursing facility and a long-term care/living facility, and the interaction of hospital stays and Medicare coverage is important. Generally, a skilled nursing facility is offered to patients when their condition can be improved and the facility's staff will set rehabilitation goals for them. If patients' goals are met or they are not improving, they will most likely be discharged. This is different from a long-term care facility, which is designed for long-term living with support through a health decline to death, and is usually funded with family funds or private long-term care insurance. One of the key nuances for skilled nursing facilities is that the costs will be covered entirely by Medicare for thirty days **only if the admission was immediately preceded by a three-day hospital stay**. If, for example, a hospital wants to discharge your parent after a two-day stay and you think a discharge to a skilled nursing facility is the right next step, you'll have to be a proactive advocate for your parent and press for a three-day stay at the hospital if the overall medical circumstances warrant it.

My suspicions are that there were some mid-level managers who were getting pressure from the bean counters to discharge my mom prior to the three-day stay period. There was seemingly some financial accounting going on with regard to direct discharges to the skilled nursing facility, which my mom obviously needed. Long story short, due to the professionalism, compassion, and understanding of the CEO, my mom's hospital stay was extended and she was then discharged directly to the skilled nursing facility, and her stay and treatment was picked up in full by Medicare.

How does this story relate to medication? Well, her crazed hallucinatory episodes that scared the daylights out of us were due to a miscommunication between her doctor's office and the hospital regarding Baclofen. Sold under the brand name Lioresal, among others, Baclofen is a medication used to treat spasticity; it's a central nervous system depressant and skeletal muscle relaxant that's also used in topical creams to help with pain. Mom's doctor meant to have her reduce her dosing after being on it for twenty years (pain mitigation from her stroke), but somehow that got lost in translation and the hospital staff just stopped giving it to her, cold turkey. I did some research on the withdrawal symptoms and found this on Wikipedia: *Withdrawal symptoms may include auditory hallucinations, visual hallucinations, tactile hallucinations, delusions, confusion, agitation, delirium, disorientation, fluctuation of consciousness, insomnia, dizziness (feeling faint), nausea, inattention, memory impairments, perceptual disturbances, pruritus/itching, anxiety, depersonalization, hypertonia, hyperthermia, formal thought disorder, psychosis, mania, mood disturbances, restlessness, and behavioral disturbances, tachycardia, seizures, tremors, autonomic dysfunction, hyperpyrexia (fever), extreme muscle rigidity resembling neuroleptic malignant syndrome and rebound spasticity.*

Holy smokes. Yes, going cold turkey after twenty years made sense of all her symptoms. In summary, I can't emphasize how important it is to understand what medications your parents are taking and feel free to dig into interactions and side effects because even professionals can make mistakes.

Paying Bills & People

Control is going to be a central theme to this entire process. Your parents will most likely be fighting to keep control of their lives and sometimes it's the little things like paying the bills or having spending money to do what they want that can mean so much to them.

Traditionally, my father had paid the bills. Of course, with the onset of dementia, he no longer had the mental capacity to work with numbers and so my mom enthusiastically took over that responsibility. She was great at it and over time this simple task kept her rooted in a sense of normalcy in a life that had transformed so quickly in so many ways. It was also great mental exercise and kept her mind sharp.

Even though she had no diagnosed cognitive impairment, over time her mental ability declined somewhat, which is normal. Your aging parent may put on appearances of being mentally acute—the "Don't worry honey, I'm okay" syndrome—and they may be doing very well. But keep in mind there may be other factors at play that you need to remember, specifically prescription drugs and loneliness. Prescription drugs (or non-prescription for that matter) may have a significant effect on the ability to focus and make rational decisions. Loneliness can cause people to make baseless personal connections with people, even salespeople, talking to them on the TV. The next thing you may find is that your parent has purchased a whole bunch of stuff she doesn't need.

One way I found to really help this scenario is to cancel the credit cards and have your parent use a prepaid debit card that can work as a credit card. The card that was recommended to me by a well-respected private fiduciary was the TrueLink Card. This is a card you can fund directly from your parent's bank account and she can't spend more than it's funded for. Thus, you don't have to worry about your parent or someone else charging thousands of dollars on a traditional credit card. You can set up alerts, have the card only work in certain categories of stores and block others. For example, you can set the card up to work at the gas station and grocery stores, but not with telemarketers. Your parent can also pull cash out at an ATM, again with the balance or withdrawal limits you set. It really gives the whole family a piece of mind that your parent will be less likely to be taken advantage of while giving her a feeling that she's still in control. In summary, a credit card can be an open door for intentional or unintentional problems and I would recommend replacing it with a TrueLink Card or something similar.

Regarding other bills, it's very easy to set up automatic payment instructions with any company providing services for your parent. There are two ways to do this with advantages and drawbacks to either method. You can either set up instructions so the service provider pulls funds from your parents' bank or you manage a bill payment system provided by their bank online and push the funds out. If the service provider is pulling in funds from your parents' bank account to pay bills it's harder to make any mistakes or miss payments but giving the authority to a service provider to pull money from your parents' bank makes some people nervous. Setting payments up on the bank side really gives more control but it's also easier to forget payments as well especially if you are busy paying your own bills.

In my case I was paying my mom's bills for awhile but I just got too busy and I didn't want to miss any payments or make any mistakes. So I ended up hiring a bill paying service. In reality it was just one woman (I'll call her Mary) that I had met who had originally worked for a CPA firm and ended up striking out on her own and she was very cost-efficient. I was able to set up a folder within the password keeper program I was using that included all of my mom's relevant websites, usernames, and passwords and shared it with her. This way Mary had instant access to my mom's bank and service providers online. Mary had all of my mom's paper bills coming to her office and all of the electronic bills coming to her email which not only helped with workflow but I had more piece of mind that there were no bills getting misplaced at my mom's house. Mary was able to send me spending reports and helped me help my mom budget and make financial decisions.

I can't stress enough how important it is to get the bill paying situation under control and if you really think you are not going to be able to dedicate the time and effort into ensuring there will be no mistakes then it really makes sense to hire a bill paying service. They can also help deter fraud and abuse by keeping an eye out for erroneous charges and of course there can be some serious consequences if your parent misses an insurance premium payment or falls behind on mortgage payments. The caveat here is that a third party will have access and control of most if not all of your parents' financial accounts so be sure to do your due diligence and hire a reputable service.

Individual Retirement Accounts (IRAs)

Regarding retirement accounts, I'll be focusing my discussion on Individual Retirement Accounts (IRAs). You might think it's an omission not discussing 401(k)s but remember that 401(k)s can be rolled over into IRAs and usually if your parent is retired they most likely will have done this already.

Most likely, at least one of your parents has an IRA, so it's worth discussing them as they can be tricky. There are generally two flavors of IRAs:

1) Traditional: These accounts usually consist of pre-tax contributions and will be taxed when funds are withdrawn at income tax rates.

2) Roth: These accounts usually consist of post-tax contributions, so there should be no tax on the funds that are withdrawn.

One of the ways I like to keep things straight in differentiating traditional and Roth IRAs is to remember that the government wants to tax your money at least once. With traditional IRAs, the contributions usually consist of funds that were deferred from work income, so they have not yet been taxed. The IRS will want its cut when money is taken out. Roth IRAs normally contain funds that have already been taxed. The government already received its cut, so no taxes should be due upon distribution. I use words like "usually" and "should" as there are always caveats you should clarify with a financial advisor. For example, traditional IRAs might also contain some post-tax contributions. The goal here is to set the framing for a discussion to help you sort out your parent's situation. So let's talk about some practical concepts regarding traditional IRAs that will most likely come into play when you're helping out your parents. I'll just refer to them as IRAs, with the understanding we are discussing traditional IRAs as opposed to Roth IRAs.

Be aware that the "Setting Every Community Up for Retirement Enhancement" Act, better known as SECURE, was recently signed into law and affects IRAs beginning in 2020. For any provision I speak about below, I will note that there has been a new change relative to this act by the following: [SECURE]

Let's start by defining some terms:

1. Required Beginning Date [of distributions] (RBD): The government has allowed contributions into and growth within the IRA to occur without being taxed. That's very gracious of the government but it's patience is not without limit. Thus, the year someone turns 72 [SECURE: changed from 70½], they are *required* to

begin distributions from the IRA by April 1 of the following year based on a formula that is usually tied to life expectancy.

2. Required Minimum Distribution (RMD): The amount of money IRA holders are required to take beginning on the RBD until they pass away.

Let's discuss IRAs with respect to three phases:

1) Accumulation/Holding Phase: The phase where no distributions are needed for retirement income

2) Distribution Phase: Any time distributions have begun, usually in retirement to supplement income (a date that can be earlier than the RBD, which we'll discuss later)

3) Post-Death Phase: A parent passes away, either with or without a surviving spouse

Accumulation/Holding Phase

Most of the questions and concerns people come to me with during this phase concern the investments. Are they appropriate given their goals, age, and needs?

The process of financial planning should be fully engaged to truly answer these questions and I encourage you to have your parents find a fee-only fiduciary financial advisor to do this. Having said that, I can impart some suggestions based on my experience and knowledge as a financial advisor.

- As people get older, many think they should transition their investment portfolios to a more conservative allocation by lowering the risk characteristics—

something often done by reducing their allocation to stocks while increasing their allocation to bonds and cash. This is not necessarily true. At age sixty, a parent might have another thirty years of living (time horizon) and that's a long time they'll need their investments working for them. For sure, lowering the risk can lower the year-by-year swings in the portfolio value (volatility), but lowering the risk characteristics of the portfolio may actually *increase* the risk of your parents running out of income before they pass away. So while many people are focused on yearly volatility risk, don't forget you need to balance that out with the risks of running out of money. Also remember that all or a significant portion of many IRAs will not be needed by your parents; instead, they might be passed to you or your children, which further increases the time horizon to not only include your parent's life, but yours and maybe even your children's as well. In summary, there is not always an automatic financial justification for investors approaching and in retirement to be overly conservative with their investments and in fact this strategy might hurt them in the long run.

- The higher the value the IRA, the larger the RMDs will be once your parent reaches RBD. In essence, your parents might be required to take out more than they need, generating a higher tax burden than expected. So, it's good to think about some options prior to the RBD. One option is to look at a Roth conversion. Essentially, it allows traditional IRA holders to convert some or all of their IRA to a Roth IRA. What does this solve? Roth IRAs have no RMDs; the government does not force an investor to take out money at 72 [SECURE] and every year thereafter because the money has already been taxed. The drawback is that when funds from a traditional IRA are converted to a Roth IRA the conversion amount is taxed at income tax rates the year of the conversion, which can be significant. And, the less living an investor has (the older they get), the more difficult it becomes to justify the savings on future taxes versus paying them today. But, for example, if a parent knows a portion of the traditional IRA will never be used in their lifetime and will be passed to beneficiaries, this might be a good time to think about converting to a Roth IRA. The bottom line is that the earlier your parents can look at this the better, and it should be done at the very least in coordinated analysis with their CPA and financial advisor.

- One of the most important things for your parents to review and update for each IRA are the beneficiary designations. A nuance of IRAs is that although they are included as part of the taxable estate, they are passed by beneficiary designation outside of a trust. For example, if your parents have a revocable family trust, you would not list the IRA as an asset of the trust. IRAs exist outside of the trust, so they do not pass to beneficiaries via the trust language in the trust (unless the trust is designated as beneficiary), but according to the beneficiary designations associated with the IRA. Every IRA your parents own should have its own beneficiary designation form associated with it and it is not enough to update just one of the forms. Each IRA account and its associated beneficiary form must have the appropriate designation information, and they don't have to be the same. Your parents will have to decide who will be primary and contingent beneficiaries, what percentages go to each, and whether the assets will pass per stirpes or per capita. It is beyond the scope of this book to get into the details, but I want to ensure you are aware of these issues so there are no surprises. Beneficiary forms are often treated lightly but in fact can have significant repercussions; your parents should review them with their estate planning attorney to ensure they get it right.

Distribution Phase

So now your parents need retirement income and they are looking at their IRAs. As explained earlier, they will be required to take distributions when they are 72 [SECURE] and every year thereafter. But, do they have to wait? No. Let's look at some options, assuming that all contributions to their IRA were pre-tax.

- Normal distribution age begins the year they turn 59½.

- Distributions are included in Modified Adjusted Gross Income (MAGI), so will add to their income for that year, thus their tax for that year.

- They can take distributions prior to age 59½ if needed, but barring any extenuating circumstances (see exceptions below), there will be an additional 10 percent penalty. This is a scenario you would prefer to have them avoid.

  - There are exceptions that will allow them to avoid a 10 percent early withdrawal penalty. One of those exceptions that you might typically see for an older parent is due to mental or physical disability and medical expenses. There are more exceptions and some qualifying and limiting factors of use, but they are worth being familiar with. If your parents need income prior to turning 59½ and need to start early withdrawals but do not qualify for any of the exceptions, they might want to look at taking "Substantially Equal Periodic Payments," otherwise known as 72(t) distributions, as the rule falls under IRS Code 72(t). Simply put, this method would allow your parents to make withdrawals prior to age 59½ without an early withdrawal penalty, but they are not without their risks. You must take these periodic payments for at least five years or until age 59½, whichever comes later, and if you run afoul of the rules there could be additional penalties on all amounts withdrawn.

○ Sometimes, older folks forget about making required estimated IRS tax payments. Or it might even be that a child has taken over this responsibility and just gets busy and forgets. In either instance, it really helps to withhold taxes on the distribution of an IRA to help avoid penalties. In my opinion, unless you or your parents have an ironclad budget and process for paying taxes, it's a best practice to pay the taxes on an IRA distribution at the time the funds are distributed. For example, if a distribution is made in March, the IRA holder might normally pay taxes sometime in the future, either for estimated quarterly or filing taxes the next year. But there's a better way to manage this if you're worried about your parent forgetting about it or not budgeting correctly. Many account custodians will be able to withhold federal and state taxes at the time cash is distributed from the IRA such that the money received is the net after-tax amount. If your parents need a hard dollar amount and you're using this technique, be sure to start with the needed dollar amount and then "gross up" for taxes. For example, if your mother needed $10,000 from her IRA for living expenses and her CPA estimated that her taxable income rate would be 20 percent, you would make a $12,000 gross distribution and withhold about $2,000, for a $10,000 net to your mom. The custodian will then account for that directly to the IRS and you're done paying taxes for that distribution—if, of course, you've estimated the withholding amount correctly. If you take this concept even further, you can increase the withholding amounts to cover a large percentage or even all of the estimated taxes for the year and into the first quarter of the next year. All these suggestions help lower the possibility of any surprise tax bills at the end of the year.

Inherited IRAs

The SECURE act made changes to how IRAs and other retirement benefits are treated when inherited. The changes are significant enough that every investor should review how their estate plans might be affected, including revising beneficiary designation forms and wills and trusts tied to IRAs.

Prior to SECURE, following the death of the IRA owner, the retirement benefits passing to a qualified beneficiary were paid over the life of the designated beneficiary. When the designated beneficiary was much younger than the IRA owner, such as a grandchild, the deferral of payments provided a significant income tax benefit, since the RMD's were calculated based on life expectancy of the grandchild or other heir.

Now, most of those inheriting an IRA in 2020 and beyond will be required to completely withdraw all plan assets within ten years of the date of death. No withdrawals have to be made during the ten-year period, but at the end of ten years from the date of the plan holder's death, the entire balance in the plan must be withdrawn. Under prior law, there was a difference in the period over which IRA assets had to be distributed based on whether the plan owner died before or after the RMD. Under SECURE, the rule requiring complete withdrawal by year ten will apply in all cases.

Exceptions to this rule are "eligible designated beneficiaries" who are still able to withdraw plan assets over their life expectancy, namely:

- Surviving spouses
- Chronically ill heirs

- Disabled heirs

Minor children are also considered eligible beneficiaries, so the ten-year payout does not apply to them. However, when the minor reaches the age of majority, the ten-year rule will then apply.

In-Home Care

Things changed dramatically for my family when my mom had a stroke at age sixty-four. One moment she had a wonderful life full of independence, activities, and dreams of more world travel. The next moment she was disabled on one side of her body; had severe pain from nerve damage; and was prescribed heavy pain relief medicine, antidepressants, blood thinners, and a concoction of other drugs that affected her life and personality in addition to the symptoms and challenges of the stroke. One moment I could walk into a happy home with the parents I grew up with who were also great friends. The next moment I had to shift my mentality to one of giver instead of taker. One from child to equal. Eventually, with both my parents, especially my father, one from child to parent.

The interesting part of this is that my mom's stroke actually strengthened my parents' relationship. Where once they might have thought a separation would give them freedom and more happiness, they now discovered their mutual support was a gift they could treasure and their years together built a richness and foundation for their lives. My father stepped up to the plate in a big way and dawdled over her to ensure she was comfortable and happy.

After a time, my father was no longer able to help my mother due to his dementia and he then became a burden for my disabled mom as he needed to be helped and supervised throughout the day. My mom was trying to hold on to the status quo, but my sister and I were able to give her some peace of mind and help her resolve some of the guilt of sending him to a cognitive care facility.

My mom was supremely stubborn, which was both a positive and negative. When I approached her with the subject of getting a more formalized care plan together, she was adamant about keeping the woman who had been working with her for years; I'll call her Mary. Mary is from Brazil and I describe her as a combination of Arnold Schwarzenegger and Mother Teresa. She was truly a blessing to our family, cared deeply for my mom, and had the strength and trustworthiness we could all rely on. My mom, of course, became emotionally attached to Mary. But there is a potential downside to having one caretaker your parent relies on. What happens during days or time periods when that caretaker is sick, needs a break, or decides to move on to another job? If you haven't prepared, you will be scrambling to get backup coverage and in the case of my mom, even one day without her caretaker was a crisis, since Mary would prepare food and serve it to her. Obviously, a scenario where your parent is not eating is not acceptable. During the periods Mary was gone on vacation, for example, her replacements were never good enough for Mom. She would always complain how the food was terrible or something wasn't done right. This was certainly a testament to Mary, but also illuminates the danger of your parent becoming too emotionally attached to one caretaker.

You'll need to get familiar with elder care companies. These are companies that have a full staff of caretakers available to provide twenty-four hours of service and just because one particular caretaker is not available at that moment doesn't mean your parents won't have care as they should have a deep bench. They will schedule caretakers to meet your needs, but don't count on having the same caretaker at all times. What you can count on is that your parent will most likely have complaints, as things are not getting done as he or she is used to having them done, and this can cause a lot of stress for everyone. But the alternative is worse, of course. Needless to say, at the very least, you should have a relationship with an elder care firm primed and ready to go either as the primary caretaker or as a backup should you have an individual who is normally working with your parent.

As a little more background, elder care companies provide services required to assist senior citizens in living as independently as possible by coming to your parents' home and helping out with anything from basic help with transportation to complex medical care. They can also provide services at non-home facilities such as a retirement home to supplement any help the facility is already providing for your parent. Because elder care covers such a broad set of services, insurance policies rarely cover all of the costs. Elder care can be costly, so it's wise for your parents to plan ahead for the day when it might be needed. Fortunately, there are public and private sources of help. The Eldercare Locator sponsored by the U.S. Administration on Aging offers information about agencies and other resources available in a given region, making it a good starting point. There tend to be a lot of good elder care companies that focus on smaller geographic areas so look to these as well as more national firms. The elder care folks I've interacted with over the years have tended to be very caring and diligent. Having said that you'll want to get references and do your due diligence as I'm sure there are some out there with less than reputable practices.

Another benefit of bringing an eldercare firm into the picture is to help a parent hear from a third-party professional. Often, experts bring an instant legitimacy to the suggestions you might have been communicating to your parent all along; that it's time to get help. In my mom's case, we brought an eldercare firm in as a backup. Their interview process was extensive and they were also able to identify holes and potential pitfalls of the current care we had in place. Ultimately, it eased my mom's resistance to what my sister and I were trying to accomplish.

Medical Alerts

It's worth discussing alert systems for your parents whether they are living alone or not. Let's start with a couple of reality checks that actually fall into the broader category of smart homes. Technology and age definitely do not mix like peanut butter and chocolate. I started testing smart home systems for my mother that can talk to you, turn on the lights, lock the door, play music, and all of the other cool stuff they advertise. The promise this technology represents is in many ways very desirable, but trying these out with my mom I found that it did not stick. Any time there was a glitch or she was lost in translation with a cloud based semi-AI she would get frustrated, upset, and say she didn't want to use it again. Granted, there was a lot of operator error, but I think a lot of her frustration was due to the fact that she wanted to use a lot of the bells and whistles but felt like a failure when she couldn't figure anything out or there was a technology issue.

Medical alerts can really help an aging parent feel safer and actually save their life. You might think they'd be okay with just a phone, but those will get lost and not be there when they need them. A home device like Alexa or Google Home seem very useful and fun, but as of the time of this writing, neither can dial 911, which is a serious drawback for the elderly. You'll need to assess whether or not your parent needs a home-only system or a mobile system they can use wherever they go. You'll also want to assess whether or not they need a system that's monitored by a service and if you feel it should have fall detection capability. Whatever the system, I recommend that it is something that can be worn on the body, around the wrist or neck, so it's close and can actually be used when needed.

When my mother got in-home care, she initially had a bell and her caretaker would come into her room when she rang it. One day, I was checking on her and heard her ringing the bell, but the caretaker was outside and didn't hear it. That prompted me to buy a battery-operated radio system. My mom had the alert button on her neck and I had the caretakers click the receiver onto their pants. This was a great solution for her and there was a strong signal throughout the house and outside, so the caretakers could hear it wherever they were. Obviously, if your parent is living alone with no caretaker, you'll need to explore a system that is somehow tied into either a landline or the internet.

Personal budgeting is also going to be a consideration and you'll want to review the contract for termination clauses and warranties. The simple system I just described was very reasonable, but with more complex systems and monitoring, the price can increase significantly. But, it might be worth it.

In summary, there's no easy solution that will fit everyone's needs, so you'll have to clarify your parent's needs, find a system that fits them within your budget, and then do some research. And finally, when you select a system, you should consider that as your parent's health deteriorates, tomorrow's needs will be different from today's, so consider a system that is easily modified without too much expense.

Home Configuration

As your parents get older, they're going to have a harder time doing things and getting around the house. If your parents have lived in their home for awhile, they'll probably have the mindset of "I've lived here for years and everything's just fine as it is." Sometimes it's hard for them to see that it's time for modifications in the home.

If your parents are thinking of selling their current home and downsizing to a smaller home, the first and most obvious configuration that is often overlooked is single versus multi-story homes. With some exceptions, it's really not ideal for the elderly to have two-story homes. Getting up and down stairs can be difficult and they are great for falls and slips, which lead to broken hips that can sometimes never be recovered from. If a multi-story home is a must, then for Pete's sake have the master bedroom and every other room needed for daily living (kitchen, bathroom, dining, etc.) on the first floor. In certain areas of the country, where real estate prices are high, this can be an issue, as builders are splitting lots to fit more thin houses, making up the square footage by building up. If your parents are currently living in a multi-story home, you'll want to talk to them about this sooner than later, because moving is not on the top of most elderly's list of things they'd like to do. They might be fine today, but there will most likely be a time in the near future that their health and ability to get around will force them to make changes when it's not convenient. I've seen elderly folks who have a more difficult time getting around second-story homes, including my parents, just stop going upstairs. That's fine *if* they have everything they need for daily living downstairs.

If their current home is where they want to be, they might just need some modifications, to include:

- Walk-in tubs with a seat and safety handle (that can easily be retrofitted into an existing home)

- Ramps for entry or in-home steps suitable for walking and in-door scooters

- Motorized chairs that lean forward and help people get out of them

- Remote switches for lighting

- Indoor elevators (if they need that second story)

- Lower counter heights (if in wheelchairs)

And finally, I'll leave you with my mom's most useful gadget that she had around the house: a jar opener. It's no way to start the day if you can't get that jam jar opened in the morning.

Assisted Living

Assisted living is independent living in a community or residential complex that gives aging adults the added benefit of care that can be personalized based on their condition. This often includes things like managing medication, preparing meals, transportation and housekeeping. You will find that the services usually provide for around the clock assistance and supervision including exercise and wellness programs in addition to transportation and meals. There is a relatively wide range of costs based on services and location and often an up front fee to join the community. With so many variables it's best to first understand what your parents' budget is within the context of their overall financial plan and then find a location that best fits their circumstances. Also remember that assisted living is not a skilled nursing facility where residents receive specialized full time care by medical staff. Costs for assisted living can vary significantly depending on the services offered which can include costs for care services, utilities, and housing.

Some parents might be very open to moving into an assisted living facility as they might enjoy a more social environment and the many activities that are provided. Other parents might be adamantly opposed to it. In my father's case, with his dementia, he was not in a state of mind to desire or oppose the transition but beyond that it was really a necessity as my mom could not care for him at home due to her disability nor did she have the financial resources to keep him home as his benefits did not cover in-home-care. My mom on the other hand was firmly committed to staying at home until her last days. It was her comfort zone and she got by with part time help until the latter days.

These are scenarios you should ensure are covered in financial plans and the costs related to each option.

End Days

Hospice

In this entire experience you go through, hospice may very well prove to be the most appreciated and heartfelt service your terminally ill parent and your family will receive. For many years, hospice was just a nebulous concept to me and I really had little appreciation for the impact it would have on me and my family. Essentially, hospice is a service provided by trained individuals either in-home or at a facility to help address the patient's physical, emotional, social, and spiritual needs. It is also there to provide relief for supporting family and caretakers. Hospice is focused on quality of life rather than length of life, which is a big distinction as I will explain. Part of quality of life, of course, is being free of pain to the extent one can be free of pain. I think I can best explain hospice by way of my experience with it as it relates to my mother.

As I explained earlier, my mother was diagnosed with terminal lung cancer and was expected to live from a few weeks to a few months. There were extensive treatments available to her that might have extended her life, but offered a questionable quality of living. At this point, my mother decided she would let nature take its course. So that's it. It was to be a period where her pain increased, her days were bedridden, and her destination was in sight and final. There are an infinite amount of emotional, physical, and spiritual issues that will arise during this time period that can exhaust not only the patient, but caregivers and family members alike. This is the time for hospice. Hospice caregivers came to the home and met with me, my sister, and my mother's caregivers to explain what could be expected, what services they were able to provide, and how to administer opium for pain. On several occasions, they brought a musician into my mom's room and she was able to listen to a pianist or flutist, with my four-year-old son getting into the action with her. Those simple moments are so impactful it's hard to fully put them into words.

One of the most important aspects was comfort for my mother. One of the most anxiety filled aspects of this lung cancer is not always the pain, but the feeling that you cannot breathe. For that, they brought in an oxygen tank and provided guidance on usage. I also found out that Medicare will cover much of the costs of hospice care and was pleasantly surprised on how well everything worked out in support of my mom in her last days.

Getting Older, Parents Dying, The Paradigm Shift

As we get older, theory becomes reality as we experience the trials life has to offer, but there is still a social and family cocoon available—enticing us with the idea that it's someone else's turn next. But then, when your parents pass away, you'll find yourself alone on a seemingly cold, windy mountaintop with a clear view of the world. And then you either consciously or subconsciously realize a paradigm shift. There's no one else. You're next.

And that, my friends, is one of the biggest challenges when your parents pass away. Your mental state is tested, along with your ability to continue on what may now be viewed as the last stage of your own life, the home stretch if you will. All your life, you've perhaps always felt your parents (or someone else) would be the one to pass away, not you. But with your parents gone, you are at the front of the line and there are no obstacles, real or imagined, to provide a buffer between you and the threshold you will at some point cross.

If you explore this concept further and find there's some truth to it as it relates to your feelings and emotional state, it's something you should consider diving into deeply through meditation, therapy, spirituality, or any other framework you might use to come to terms with this shift. Without some resolution of this change in perspective (whether conscious or unconscious), there is a possibility of entering a potential long period of depression.

What happens when our parents die? My theory is that for most of us, we're surrounded by a construction of safety—both real and not real—which by virtue of its nature, makes danger and death appear to be far away. This is fine to a certain extent, as early on I think the role of parents is to make their children feel safe and loved. Somewhere along the path in the transition from kids to young adults, we learn that Santa Claus is not real and there is danger and death awaiting all. Learning the realities of life and preparing how to deal with them at the right time are essential to growing up.

That's why the role reversal from child of the parent to parent of the parent becomes difficult for many people. A parent can be described as a caregiver of a child. What happens later on in life is that the challenge of being a caregiver to your parent(s) presents itself—thus the idea of being a parent to your parent.

Your Search For Understanding

Coping with the decline and death of a parent can be a devastating journey—one that often induces depression, family arguments, and overwhelming legal and administrative hurdles to overcome. If you are fortunate to live a relatively long life, chances are you will be faced with these challenges.

Many of us are at an age where parents are declining in health and passing away. We all have the knowledge that sooner or later we will make the ultimate life transition, but it's usually just an occasional whisper in our consciousness. When a mental or physical decline shows itself, there is often an effort by patients to maintain the status quo (denial); this can even occur when there is a definitive short-term terminal diagnosis. For family members, this is the time where the reality of the end of life begins to hit home and the voice in your head begins to speak with the phrase you hoped never to hear: "Here it comes." If you are not properly prepared physically, mentally, and administratively, the burden of what you'll have to go through can be overwhelming.

Another critical aspect of this process is that it will not be happening in a void. Most of you will be dealing with this while working and taking care of your own kids. Keeping things together in your household, maybe with you and your significant other working and dealing with the demands of raising a family, is enough for anyone. But when you throw in the additional burden of taking care of parents, you increase the probability that the whole house of cards could come tumbling down. Add in the fact that it's not just your parents you may be dealing with—but siblings, in-laws, step-parents, etc.— and you can see it's a potentially overwhelming life proposition.

It's the big squeeze. If you are in this position, you are part of Generation Squeezed™.

The good news is that you can transform this process from one that results in chaos to an experience that's rewarding for you and your family—and gives you peace of mind. I can promise you you'll get a better feeling of peace and satisfaction in honoring your parents' life work by ensuring their affairs are settled smoothly. And, if you have personal hurdles in discussing these issues with your parents, or they're providing pushback, remind yourself and them of this guiding rationale behind your efforts:

Consider the work as honoring your parents' lives by ensuring their legacy and affairs are settled honorably, efficiently, and with care.

With this in mind, I hope your perspective on the road ahead will be transformed from one of dread and stress to one of purpose and fulfillment that provides long-term happiness for you and your family. The key to remember is that this transformational perspective has to be supported by a lot of work, or else your head-in-the-clouds bliss will surely be hammered by hail and high winds. When it comes to life advice, if people say you can transform your life by a paradigm shift in your mental perspective, they are both right and wrong. Certainly your mental perspective can create and destroy your dreams and life's work. Without practical advice and right effort, though, your mental state will be challenged at every corner.

The point is this: it's one of life's greatest ironies that if you aren't careful, caring for aging and dying parents in many cases accelerates your own path toward decline and death.

The odds are high that you will have additional major stress factors within the same years. Some of these factors are chance occurrences in life and some are actually a result of people spending more time and energy on their parents such that, for example, it affects their job and they lose it. You can then see that if you're not careful, life can get out of hand quickly and conspire to bring you down to the depths of an uncharted valley.

I've found that first acknowledging and reflecting on this phenomenon is helpful. Like anything, accepting the truth as it is always advantageous. It may be uncomfortable at first, but it's always helpful in the long run. My go-to framework for insight and management of issues of the mind and heart has been the teachings and meditative techniques of Theravada Buddhism—and also physical exercise: surfing, running, and jiu jitsu. Having said that, I've also tried to cull insight and motivation from the almost infinite sources of inspiration and lessons that have been transmitted over the millennia and are continually presented by life. In fact, the process of being a caregiver in various capacities for my parents has in itself taught me much and given me a better understanding of life.

On an August Sunday morning, I got the call that my father had passed. My first thought was that I should have known and stayed there and been there with him. I felt bad that I had not been there with him during his last moments.

This is a scenario worth exploring. With a family, job, and a life, it is nearly impossible to keep a twenty-four-hour vigil on your own. To be there at the time of death, you have to predict the day, hour, minute, and second—and that is impossible.

Sometimes you think it will be any day and then it takes years. Other times you think it will take years and it happens suddenly.

Even though I was the only sibling or relative who lived close by, I knew I was not going to be able to be there all the time. So I did my best. There are some strange emotions and thoughts that can go through your mind during this time. Sometimes you feel like you're just a vulture waiting for the inevitable when you realize that given the circumstances, a quicker passing would be better than a long, drawn-out period of suffering. That's one of the reasons it's important to understand your parent's mindset prior to the later stages of illness—whether or not the most robust life-prolonging drugs and technology should be used or once a certain point has been reached, the transition should be made as swift as possible. If, for example, your father or mother does not wish to prolong their passing, you can take some comfort in understanding that it's their will to pass away. If you can somehow accept the beauty of life, the inevitability of death, and the mysterious wonder of the universe we are beholden to, you just might come to terms with any thoughts of wanting a life to end. So, it's possible to keep a constant vigil, but realize it may last hours, days, weeks, months, or years—and may not be feasible. At the very least, do the best you can, committing not to second-guess yourself after the fact.

On my drive and arrival at the facility on that early Sunday morning of my dad's passing, I was acutely aware that the world had not skipped a beat. Surfers were heading to the beach. People were hitting the coffee shops. Kids were across the street in the park playing soccer. No one noticed. No one noticed my father had died. No one noticed my sadness. It was a confirmation for me about the nature of life; my loss was one of the most significant things in my life, but of little significance to the rest of the world.

I had asked the staff to leave my dad in bed so I could have some time alone with him. Opening the door, I looked at my father's corpse—a defeated body with a vacant stare lay there in this nondescript room—a sharp contrast to the robust force of life I had known and loved who anchored our family life. I sat next to him and began to meditate. One aspect of the meditation was to reflect on the love we had for each other. Another was giving thanks for the love and support he had given me and my family. The last aspect was a final giving of Metta and encouragement to help his transition and journey into the next phase. I felt a togetherness and knew our spirits would always be intertwined. And with that, I left. My father, as I knew him as a parent and friend, was physically gone, but on a spiritual level, he was not gone. He would always be with me.

When you think about it, death is the singularly most lonely event in our lives. In birth, we arrive in a collaborative exercise with our mothers, who push us out to a new world surrounded by people. Throughout life we are surrounded by all the things our world has to offer. We may on occasion do things in solitude, but there is always someone there to walk with us if needed. In death, we have to transition through the door in absolute solitude. No one can make that journey with us.

The mere thought of death and this prospect of a lonely transition can bring a lot of anxiety for many people. There is something known as "death meditation," where you essentially practice dying. It's focused on ensuring you're not surprised by an event you know is going to happen, but are familiar with it.

Thus, when it does happen, you can hopefully have a calmer, peaceful experience—which might help your transition into wherever you may go. You might think of this as a morbid idea, but just realize the more you practice anything, the more confidence you will have. A good analogy might be the programs airlines have set up for people who have an inexplicable fear of flying. They actually get them in an aircraft model and simulate the flying experience so they can overcome, or at least lessen, their fears. If you're inclined to try this exercise as it relates to death, give it a try and seed the idea with your parents.

After my father passed away, I think the reality of my mom being on her own hit her and she became somewhat scared as to how everything was going to play out. Surviving spouses will act differently. Some will go into a shell and get depressed. Some will blossom with the release of stress. Perhaps the relationship was perceived as being a burden and the deceased spouse as overbearing and a new personality aspect will emerge. You just never know. The first thing to remember is that you should not pin your expectations on how you think your surviving parent *should* be acting. Of course, you are free to judge and act according to your own values, but ultimately it's their life and you for sure don't know everything that went on in their lives and relationships. If you come from a perspective of compassion, it will help you deal with any unexpected ways your surviving parent might act. This, I might add, is a good rule in life in general. However, it does not mean anything goes and everything is okay.

After the death of one of your parents, you may find your surviving parent will need a lot more help. My old-school, Depression-era disabled mom just got tougher and tried to project that she did not need any help. This stubbornness to cling to the status quo and perhaps maintain some purpose in life caused a few dynamic conversations between the two of us. Thankfully, I have a wonderful, wise, and insightful sister who was able to balance out my tendencies to just fix problems as I see them with some intuitive reminders on my mom's nature and the shortcomings of my approach. The yin and yang of wise siblings really does help.

When Your Parent Passes

If you're reading this book and one of your parents has just passed, you'll either be laser focused or in fog. Either way it's best to have a checklist of all of the things you'll need to take care of and you can find plenty of these by simply searching the internet and I urge you to do so as soon as possible. If you're in charge, you might be tempted to share the checklist with your siblings or other interested parties to share the load. This might work out fine and having help can be a great thing during this difficult time. But, delegating responsibilities can also cause a lot of problems if things are done right or just not done at all. I'd just like to comment on two issues that I think are worth expanding on amongst the many things that you'll have to take care of.

Obtaining Death Certificates: It's very important to get multiple certified copies of the death certificate. You'll hit a wall administratively if you don't. Every situation will be different, but don't hesitate to get at least twelve copies.

Reporting Death To The Social Security Administration: It's very important to notify Social Security as soon as possible. Most funeral homes will do this, but don't leave it to chance.

There is a whole chain of implications with regard to benefits that occur when it receives notice. There are a couple of things to know about Social Security benefits. First, they are paid in arrears, i.e., June's benefits are paid in July. Second, Social Security regulations require that a person live an entire month to receive benefits for that month. Let me clear things up by way of an example. Let's say your parent received a Social Security payment in the beginning of June and died on June 20. Your parent *would* be entitled to that benefit payment received in June, as it was paid in arrears for the month of May. They would not be entitled to a July payment (a June benefit), since they were not living for the entire month of June. Obviously, they are not entitled to any payments from July moving forward. You don't want your parent's account to continue to receive these Social Security payments, as the estate will have to remit them back to the SSA and things could get messy.

Grieving & Depression

You'll want to understand that there is a difference between grieving and depression. It's been said that life really is a constant struggle against extreme hardship in a chaotic world that ultimately leads to death. So, life itself is full of factors that may bring forth grief or depression. It just so happens that the death of a loved one is merely a particular sure-to-happen event within the scope of all life events. Thus, the idea I mentioned earlier, that you must have the tools to observe, understand, and work through life's struggles, becomes important not only when losing a loved one, but is really an essential ingredient for a fulfilling, robust life. It just so happens that the death of a parent is often a very strong moment that may not be able to be hidden away or dealt with casually like other hardships in life. It's significantly more than a flat tire or a lost cell phone if your parents are truly meaningful to you.

Grief and depression are complex psychological symptoms that are best analyzed by medical professionals. How you pull yourself out of these periods will depend on many factors. I've spoken a lot about how spiritual factors and tools along with your general psychological disposition can go a long way to help you persevere. Having said that, there is unfortunately plenty of evidence that many psychological issues are due to chemical and hormonal imbalances that cannot be completely counteracted without medical intervention.

You could think of grief as depression-lite.

When a parent dies, you will go through a grieving period. It may be long. It may be short. The thing to note is that there is no single official certified grieving period. Different cultures grieve in different ways for different amounts of time, often defined by religious practices. For example, the Toroja, an indigenous people in Indonesia, sometimes wait months or years after a death before a funeral ceremony takes place— often caring for a mummified relative in their home. This is partly in order for the family to raise funds for the cost of the funeral expenses. so the deceased's family can raise the significant funds needed to cover funeral expenses. Torajans believe that a death is not necessarily a sudden event but a more gradual journey to the afterlife.

From our perspective, this is an extraordinary process, but it highlights the idea that you should not be overly constrained by preconceived notions of how to grieve or get too caught up with what's "normal" or not. You are unique and can process things in your own unique way.

After the structured ceremonial aspect of death is over, you're still left with yourself. If you have a memorial service with friends and relatives, you'll be comforted by the support. But in the grand scheme of events, this moment will come and go in a flash and you will be left to your own devices.

Sometimes being left to your own devices can mean that you can get depressed and necessitate the need for medical and/or psychological help. Some of the symptoms you'll want to be aware of include

- Finding it difficult to perform your daily duties

- Wishing that you had died

- Feeling like you have no purpose in life

- Not being interested in social activities

A study at Stanford stated that depression is a normal response to the loss of a parent. Having said that, it also noted that those dwelling excessively on negative emotions as a result of the loss are at risk for long-term depression. The study goes on to say that people who have recovered from a grief-related event within one month tend not to lapse into depression months later. The takeaway from this is to not think that if you have been grieving for forty days you are going to immediately and certainly lapse into depression; rather, that it's relatively healthier to have a shorter grieving period than a longer one. Additionally, as I mentioned earlier, in life, events good and bad seem often to come in groups. The study noted that on average, people who lost a loved one also reported four additional major stress factors within the same year. So it's important to remember that you won't be dealing with this event in isolation and hopefully you can understand the importance of being prepared.

You need to find the right balance between taking the time to process a loss and focusing disproportionately on it. It's a balancing act and everyone will have their own methods and time frame—but be aware that an endless focus on grief can have significant long-term negative effects on your well-being.

I think it's also important to be prepared for people to not act as expected. What might be one of the most impactful moments in your life is likely only a blip in the life of people you know. Friends and extended family lead busy lives and fight their own battles, just like you. If you have the expectation that they will come running to your door with boundless support, you will most likely be setting yourself up for a letdown. As with anything in life, having a preconceived notion of how others should act is a sure way to set the stage for a lot more grief. Let people express themselves to you in the way they see fit and move on without judgment. If I had my druthers, though, 'I'd never see another "sorry for your loss" comment on Facebook.

There's a very funny moment in a "Curb Your Enthusiasm" episode in which Larry David introduces the concept of "the sorry window." The conversation goes something like this:

> Friend: "I know what you must be going through because my dad died about two years ago."

> Larry: "Huh." (He takes a sip out of his drink and starts reading his book again.)

Friend: "What was that? That's all you have to say when I tell you my father died?"

Larry: "What should I have said?"

Friend: "I'm sorry to hear that? Sad news?"

Larry: "With all due respect, don't you think the sorry window has closed on that?"

Friend: "The sorry window? I didn't know there was a sorry window."

Larry: "Two years. You're still getting sorrys? I don't think so."

Remember, life will move on virtually uninterrupted for most of your friends and relatives when your parent dies. At some point, you'll want to move on as well. Just remember that moving on does not necessarily mean leaving. As I said before when I discussed my father's death, he was gone but he will always be with me. The window is always open in my heart; it's just the sorry part I've let go. It is really a yin and yang perspective.

And You Are...?

Your parents have passed away and you've decided to roll up your sleeves and help either formally or informally, depending on the circumstances. You decide to start with an easy one and cancel the cable TV service. The service representative listens to your predicament and kindly apologizes for your loss and then asks, "And you are..."? Well, you're the son or daughter and you're trying to get things done and the representative says, "Well, prove it." I'm being a little facetious, of course, and you certainly don't want someone without authority giving orders to the cable company, investment firm, mortgage company, etc. But who are you? Well, you might in fact just be the son or daughter with no authority to do anything at all. You also might have been given authority to act formally in certain ways, as we previously discussed, but it's also worth laying out the distinctions of what types of titles exist under differing circumstances. Note that the last two duties (conservator and attorney-in-fact) would typically be used while your parent(s) are living, but it's good to see them all listed together.

Trustee

A trustee is appointed by what is called the maker of a trust and carries out the terms of the trust that are laid out in a trust document.

- One would only need a trustee when there is a trust

- When the original trustee is no longer managing a trust, for any reason, a successor trustee will take responsibility.

Personal Representative

A personal representative is just a term for an executor for the estate of someone who left a will. It is also the term used for an administrator of an estate if there is no will. The probate court supervises personal representatives.

Administrator of the Estate

The administrator of the estate is a person appointed to act on behalf of the estate If a person dies without a will or living trust then an administrator is appointed. An administrator is also appointed when a person dies with a will but the person who had been named as executor is unable to perform their duties.

Attorney-In-Fact

An attorney-in-fact is appointed via a Durable Power of Attorney to handle the financial affairs of someone unable or unwilling to do so themselves.

Executor of the Estate

The executor of the estate makes decisions and acts on behalf of the estate of a deceased person.

Conservator of the Estate

A conservator is appointed by the probate court to handle the financial affairs of a person who can no longer do so.

Even when you have all your ducks in a row, you'll still be frustrated by some of the experiences you'll have even for some of the mundane things that need to get done. Case in point, recently a cable TV company charged the estate of a 102-year-old woman an early termination fee after the woman's death. Technically, the cable account was in the deceased's daughter's name and the cable company finally apologized, but...jeez.

Remember, though, your parents or the courts may not have appointed you or any of your siblings to have any formal responsibility whatsoever. And in many circumstances this might be an ideal scenario.

Let's start by discussing the rationale behind your parent naming a professional third-party representative to an estate, typically put in place within the verbiage of a trust. Another way of looking at it: what are the potential pitfalls of appointing a child, family member, or friend (for simplicity, I'll just use the word "child" to represent this group) as any one of the appointees listed above?

1. The appointed child may not have the expertise to properly execute their duties. There are a lot of complications that can arise when, for example, taxes aren't paid, final IRA RMDs aren't distributed, etc.

2. The appointed child may have the expertise to properly execute the duties, but down the road when they are actually needed to perform, they might be too busy, sick, on vacation, or have passed away.

3. The child may be ready, willing, and able, but excessively influenced by spouses, family members, and personal agendas that conflict with the expressed intent of the trust. This will most likely cause legal challenges and result in a mess for everyone.

What are the options for parents to avoid these issues? With regard to a trust, there are two common options: appoint a corporate trustee or a private fiduciary. By appointing either of these, your parent can avoid the issues listed above almost entirely. There will of course be a cost to hiring either of these, but the value may very well be worth it.

You might be more familiar with a corporate trustee, as they tend to be affiliated with larger national institutions often affiliated with banks. In my experience, they are very good with larger complex estates and have more services under one roof. One of the drawbacks I've seen for any services company with an "everything under one roof" business model is that they may have some conflicts of interest selling products and services you need to keep your eyes open for. Larger organizations may not have the local representation and personal touch someone might want, which can cause additional administrative drag on the process. Having said that, some are very good at what they do.

Many people are not familiar with private or professional fiduciaries. For clarity, a fiduciary is someone who has been placed in the highest confidence to protect and manage and protect the affairs of a person. They also help ensure their wellbeing both mentally and physically. Within the context of probate law, a professional fiduciary should manage the estate of a person who has passed away and/or manage the care of someone who is still living who cannot manage their affairs on their own.

Getting Your Kids Through The Process

Let me first say that it can be very dangerous trying to compare and criticize other parents through your own lens with its particular filter on values and perspectives. Having said that, I'm a proponent of the idea that you don't want your kids growing up to be a person you don't like and respect. With that comes a lot of responsibility involving immediate and clear feedback. In fact, recently there have been a lot of moments where I put more thought into how and why I'm raising my son than I put into how and why I'm living my life. Granted, I've put a significant amount of time and effort into sorting out my values and goals, but it just goes to show that for many parents the burden is heavy and taken seriously.

I'm an older father and thus my son experienced the death of my mom at a rather young age—four years old. So I was thinking very hard on how to handle the situation. My first approach was to think about life and what ultimately does us the best in the long run. Simply stated, it's the truth. For sure the truth can be tough at first. More than tough, it can challenge your whole life perspective and cause a complete reassessment of the meaning of everything. Although the truth might be difficult to comprehend and seem like not the best approach at the moment, in the long run it has a way of elevating our emotional intelligence, wisdom, and understanding.

The flip side of the coin was my son's age during my mom's terminal cancer decline and death. He believed in Santa Claus and I was positively a lead co-conspirator in the charade. Rather than tell him there were really no such things as monsters, I would oblige him when the lights went out at bedtime and check for monsters in his room with a flashlight, paying particular attention to the behind-the-door monsters and the camouflage monsters on the wall, as directed. And of course, the Easter bunny laid all those eggs. Why? Well, I justify my actions with my idea that these stories inspire some creativity and imagination and socialize our kids into our culture. Myths and stories, if framed correctly, can teach our children a lot. But it's a delicate balance and you don't want to take it too far or too broadly. At some point, he'll find out there is no Santa Claus and he'll be as disappointed as every other kid out there. Of course, if he was originally told the truth, that there was no Santa Claus, he would have avoided the letdown. What the heck; Santa Claus is awesome, so there you have it. Overthinking things has its downside as well and not much makes a parent happier than seeing a happy kid. We're suckers for it.

What I realized with my son early on was that he was very good at listening to explanations, processing them, and understanding—at least in his own way. And, my suspicion is that most kids, regardless of their age, are better than we adults think they are at this. There's a point when a kid is a toddler and he or she is just bouncing around doing things and needing clear direct directions just to survive. Stay out of the street! Don't spill your milk! You're going to bed because it's bedtime! Hold my hand now! Then the transition from toddler phase to "why" phase came. I was a little slow on the uptake and so he would get frustrated sometimes because I was still operating in toddler dad mode, then I would get frustrated, and the wheel turned that way. Then I realized things were changing and I had to change my approach. So, when he would get frustrated at something, rather than just bark orders, I instituted "the talking chair." Maybe he'd be crying and frustrated at something and I'd take him by the hand and say, "Let's go to the talking chair." He had his chair, I had mine, and I clearly explained that it was a safe zone where neither of us would be angry or could get into trouble for what we said. We sat facing each other and I would then calmly ask him what was wrong, give him a chance to explain, and then explain to him why we were approaching that particular situation in a given way. Every time, it ended with him saying, "Okay, I understand, thank you for talking with me," and jumping out of the chair—and the moment was gone.

So, that, I discovered, was my four-year-old son's nature. With that in mind, I decided to explain very clearly what was happening to his grandmother, that she was sick, and she would die soon.

And then came many questions and statements from my son: *What is death? Where do we go? Do we come back? How was I made? Will I die? Will you die? I don't want you to die. I'm sad. I understand. Let's go help grandma.*

Hopefully, you can see that you'll need to be prepared. The conversations will go on tangents to places that are hard to explain and get your own mind around, much less for children. Of course, the path of least resistance is to say that grandma went on a long vacation. Convenient, but of course not true, and totally misses many moments of discovery with your child. At the end of the day, take the approach you deem best for your child; I wouldn't begin to judge. But remember that our words and actions have long-lasting effects on our children and if approached the right way, will have many benefits to your relationship. It's another reminder that you're being squeezed with the pressure of your aging and dying parent and the responsibilities of your family life, but with the right enlightened approach, you can transform the experience to be positive for you and your family in the long run.

And I'll leave you with this. As my son was processing all of this and on one of his many Q&A sessions with me, he told me something that hit me right in the center of my heart. "Daddy, before I was born, I was looking for you." Man. That still gets me just writing it. And, I would never have known had I not been talking to him about these things. I'm sure glad I did.

Settling The Estate

Valuations

After both parents pass away, the executor of the estate, which might be you, will have to value it. If the estate consists of traditional investment accounts, bank accounts, and the home they lived in, then this process is quite simple. You just need to clarify the value of the assets on the date of the last death. This is usually very easy with traditional investment and bank accounts, as you can easily look at statements or call the financial institution for statements. Again, realize you'll most likely need to provide them with a copy of the death certificate and have evidence you have authority to act on behalf of the estate. With real estate, you'll essentially have to get the value appraised, preferably by a licensed appraiser, which should cost several hundred dollars.

Things get much more complicated when there are businesses, multiple residential and/or commercial real estate holdings, and complex investments. In these cases, many of the holdings might have an up-to-date valuation, but most likely there will be significant holdings whose valuations need to be established. In these cases you might need to hire a valuations professional.

Step Up In Basis

A step up in basis is one of the best ways for a family to save taxes on an appreciated asset that is passed down after death. This concept is important to understand, so let's talk about it at a high level.

Let's start by understanding what basis is. If you purchase an asset, your purchase price is your cost basis. For example, if you buy shares of a stock for $10,000, then $10,000 would be your cost basis—often simply referred to as basis. When you sell that asset, you'll determine if and how much you'll be taxed based on the selling price relative to the basis. In our example, if you sold the stock for $15,000 ($5,000 above your basis), you would have a gain of $5,000. That gain would be reported and you would apply your appropriate tax rate to it to determine your tax.

Our parents often have assets like real estate and investment portfolios that were purchased years ago and have appreciated from their original purchase price, or basis. If they were to sell the assets prior to their death, they would be taxed on the gain, the difference between their basis and the selling price. For example, if they bought investments for $1,000,0000 and then sold them for $2,000,0000, they would be taxed on the gain of $1,000,000, which could end up being a lot of money. Now let's say your parents pass away and you inherit that same asset, which on the date of death was again valued at $2,000,000. If *you* sell it, there would be no gain, or no tax! How is that possible? It's due to the step up in basis law. When assets are passed to a beneficiary, the basis of the inherited asset steps up from the original purchase price to the price on the date of death. Any gain on the investment after the step up in basis is on you, but that's a much better scenario than if your basis was your parents' original purchase price.

What this means is that if you inherited this asset, you could either hold onto it, knowing if it continues to appreciate you wouldn't get as impacted with taxes from a future sale if the step up in basis law were not on the books. Alternatively, you could sell immediately with no tax on the gain that occured while your parent was still living.

This concept is applicable for almost any asset. For example, if your parents had an investment account, typically you as the heir would provide the custodian company proof of identity along with a death certificate, probate court order, or other documentation to get the shares stepped up. The custodian would either transfer the shares to an account in your name or sell the shares and send the proceeds to you.

There may be reasons not to wait or do things differently via trust and charitable strategies, which are beyond the scope of this discussion. It's worthwhile for your parents to discuss these issues with their financial advisor, estate planning attorneys, and tax advisors (all of them) to come up with a cohesive, intelligent, and cost-effective game plan, depending on the type and value of the assets.

Taxes

Let me preface this section with the comment that taxes can be complex and the advice I'm giving should not be construed as tax advice; definitely consult with your tax advisor when dealing with taxes. It's better to use an expert and get it 100 percent right than doing it yourself and getting it 95 percent right. It's that 5 percent you might get wrong that could cause you some big headaches.

Let's clarify that there will generally be two tax areas that need to be considered after your last parent has passed: income *and* estate taxes.

The first scenario is the situation where your parents have been married and filing jointly and one parent has passed away. Tax filing the year of death will essentially be a continuation of the status quo, where the surviving spouse continues to pay federal and state (if applicable) income taxes for the household. When filling out tax forms, make sure your surviving parent makes a note on the return that their spouse is deceased. According to the IRS, you do not need to file any additional forms to claim your refund when filing jointly with a deceased spouse. Generally, there should be no estate taxes due upon the death of the first spouse.

The second scenario is when your last surviving parent passes away. In this case, remember that not only will you or a representative of the estate need to pay the year's income taxes, but you or a representative might also have to pay estate taxes as well. How will you know if you need to pay estate taxes? Well, this is where things can get quite involved and it's best to coordinate all of this with your parent's estate planning attorney and CPA to make sure everyone is on the same page.

In general, you'll have to inventory all assets and liabilities and determine the net worth of the estate. Depending on what kind of estate planning was done, it may appear that some assets were your parents but maybe they're not. For example, if they created a living or family trust, which are generally revocable, then these assets would most likely be counted as part of the estate valuation. But during their lifetime, your parents might have transferred some of their assets to an irrevocable trust that might put those assets outside of the estate and not count as part of the estate valuation.

Another thing to remember that often catches people is that usually life insurance benefits come to the beneficiaries tax-free. For example, if your mother who was the last surviving parent had a $1,000,000 life insurance policy with you as the beneficiary, you will in most cases receive that benefit income tax-free to you. But, also in most cases, that benefit value will be included as part of the valuation of your parent's estate unless that life insurance policy was previously transferred to an Irrevocable Life Insurance Trust (ILIT).

Now that you have an estate value, you have to pay estate taxes, correct? Well no, not necessarily. According to the IRS the gift and estate tax exemption is $11.58 million for 2020. That means that an individual can leave $11.58 million to heirs and pay no federal estate or gift tax, while a married couple will be able to shield $23.16 million.

As you can see, things can get complicated very quickly and we're just touching the surface. I've also just been discussing relatively simple scenarios where your parents had things fairly well organized with wills, trusts, and all their estate planning documents in order. The situation gets orders of magnitude more difficult and complicated when there are no wills or trusts and you need to go to the courts to establish personal representatives, etc. Further analysis also needs to take into account any gifting that occured during their life that may affect their estate exclusion amounts and/or they might have business ownership in business structures that may or may not be part of the estate. I hope these are more data points to help motivate you and your parents in getting their affairs squared away prior to something happening.

As a final note, don't be too eager or let a family member encourage you to quickly distribute all the assets when settling an estate. You should have a holdback reserve of cash so you can be sure all debts, funeral expenses, professional fees, and estate and income taxes can be paid. If you were in charge of settling the estate, it might be hard to give a brother or sister a call and tell them you messed up and you need $10,000 returned to the estate to pay a lingering bill for the estate. You most likely will find that it will have magically disappeared.

Estate Sale

Stuff. What do you do with all the stuff? You've been given the responsibility of selling the personal property of a loved one; what in the heck do you do now? Perhaps your parent had laid out who gets what or you and your siblings worked together to figure it out. This might turn out to be a situation where no one is perfectly content with the results, but at least you can agree on a process, something as simple as seeing who goes first and just let family members go down the list and pick what they want; like a professional sports draft. For some items, this might be easy. Other items that might have no significance to one person might have deeply emotional connotations to someone else. Once the initial process of dividing parent belongings among family members and friends is finished, you'll still probably find there are a lot of things left over that no one really wanted or can practically fit in their homes. This is where you have to have an estate sale, which in itself can be stressful. Someone has to be in charge and if it's you and you're doing it yourself, be prepared for another full-time job of taking pictures, figuring out pricing, coordinating and advertising the sale, getting a petty cash bank and credit card reader, haggling with buyers, making sure random strangers aren't coming into your parents' house to steal stuff—the list goes on. After that, you may have to continue posting stuff individually online and be dealing with texts, phone calls, and emails ad nauseum.

Some of you might really enjoy the process, but I did not. Thankfully, my sister helped immensely *and* I was lucky enough to have a good friend who is in the business of doing estate sales advise me on the process and help me price unique items.

If you decide you need help, who do you turn to? Let's talk about a couple of different options.

Auctioneer

Auctioneers have a specific purpose. They will walk through your home and select those items they feel would be appropriate for their particular auctions. This might be perfect for you or not. Some auction houses might be focused on high-end art, which would most likely leave a significant amount of personal items to be dealt with. Realize that depending on the auction rules, you may not get anything close to the value you thought you were getting. Auctions are typically of limited duration, you'll probably have to pay shipping costs, and payment upon sale—if there is a sale—might take longer than you expected.

Estate Liquidator

When you're settling your parents estate, you may have many legitimate reasons to hurry the process along. For example, you might need to do a remodel or freshen up the home to rent it for cash flow needs or get it ready for sale as soon as possible.

An estate liquidator (EL) can usually help you with most aspects of the disposition of personal items in an efficient manner. The first question any EL worth their salt should ask you is whether or not you are the trustee or authorized/appointed agent of the deceased person or trust. They should also ask you for notarized documentation. And, you should provide this documentation to them enthusiastically. First, you'll give the EL the confidence that he's dealing with someone who has authority to make decisions. Second, you certainly don't want other family members or nefarious characters interjecting themselves into the process and mucking up the waters. It could get ugly without that documentation.

The next thing you need to do is to go through the home with family and friends and separate any items of sentimentality. Any personal items, whether they be pictures, a shirt, a couch, etc. that you don't want to sell should be boxed up or separated and taken out of the home. The easiest way to do this is to just get post-it notes and have each person place them on items they want. There will often be items more than one person wants and if things start getting contentious or complicated, just do "paper- scissors-rock" to see who goes first and go down the list. Now it might be the case where someone places his name on a million dollar diamond necklace, so barring any specific language in a trust or will, it's up to you as trustee to determine if allowing that person to have that item would be in the best interest of the trust and/or beneficiaries.

Once all this is accomplished, it's a good idea to talk to an EL and get that person over to the house. He or she will be able to look at all the personal items that are left and determine the best path forward for an estate sale.

During an estate sale, you'll have complete strangers walking through your parents' home opening drawers and looking at everything. I found most were very respectful, but you'll have to come to grips with the fact that they'll just be doing their thing on a not so special day and invading a space that might have deep emotional meaning to you. If you think you're going to have a hard time with strangers invading your sacred space, think about not being there for the estate sale. One decision that might mitigate the issues of random strangers coming to the home is having a private versus a public estate sale.

One other tip. I mentioned that people will be going through drawers. I would suggest sanitizing the house and removing any documentation with confidential information on it or anything you would not want other people to see.

Memorial & Burial/Cremation

Our family has a plot in a New Hampshire cemetery with headstones of Smiths going back to the 1600s. It's kind of a lonely place and it hits me on the occasions I have visited that all the people whose names are on those headstones with the exception of my grandfather, grandmother, father, and mother are forgotten. I keep hearing people say things like, "Never forgotten. Always remembered," but the reality is most of us will only be remembered as long as there is someone living who has known us. But we do what we can and must do to celebrate and remember, because even a little bit of closure is good.

A funeral requires a lot of important decisions, some of which are:

- Whether to bury or cremate the deceased
- Whether to hold a traditional funeral service or memorial service or both
- Whether to follow any religious traditions
- Where the interment or service should take place

That's a lot to organize, and when you add family drama into the situation, things can get colorful. In cases of cultural intermarriage, religious difference, geographic distance, or family division as a result of divorce or disagreement, it can get very messy.

When it comes to a burial, there are essentially two ends of the spectrum and everything in between. On one end, there are no prior arrangements and no direction (usually because of no will). If the deceased didn't make any preferences legally known, then the decision falls to the next of kin or nearest relative. If the next of kin is unavailable or unable to make decisions, then you just go down the list with relatives until someone who is able to make these decisions can be found.

On the other end of the spectrum is a situation where all the details are laid out clearly and everything is prepaid by your parents. Usually there will be stipulations in a living will, last will and testament, or other legal or notarized document. The point is, there are several ways to get authority to get things done; you'll just have to have the right paperwork to do so.

A comment on prepaid cremation services is worthwhile. Both my mother and father had prepaid services and they worked really well; I was very happy with their services. They picked up my deceased parents' bodies at the mortuary and delivered the ashes with a nice box and flag—all very well done. It was just one other administrative and logistical burden my father had the foresight to take off my plate. On the other hand, I spoke with someone from the same company to clarify its costs and services for my own purposes. I asked to see the contract before signing because, well, never sign a contract without reading it and I wanted to fully understand the services and fees. I was informed it was their policy not to send out contracts for review until they were signed by the customer. That, of course, absolutely misses the point of reviewing a contract and seemed sketchy to me; since then, I have yet to move forward on it. Maybe I just got the wrong person, I don't know, we'll see. The point being, buyer beware.

On a final note, one or both of your parents might have served in the military and have benefits available to them from either the VA or state-specific benefits. Be sure to check with the VA for any military benefits that might be available for burial location and other services.

Your Personal Voyage: a Timeless Classic

The Odyssey, the ancient greek story of Odysseus' travels and return home, is recognized as a classic steeped in our collective mythology. Believed to be written in the 8th century BC, it is one of the oldest and well-known stories of Western civilization. Odysseus battles and is befriended by Greek gods and it took him ten years to return home to be confronted with further trials and tribulations.

Whether life has separated you from your parents because of, well, life, or if you've made a more proactive effort to make that happen—or vice versa—the onset of aging and death of a parent will find you, like Odysseus, making a journey back home in some way or another.

Since myths can be viewed as truths that are weaved into stories, it's worth considering the perspective that your life is part of the fabric of our collective mythology. Within your life voyage, it's the return home that often seems to be most impactful and potentially full of so many emotional and practical implications. No, you cannot really ever go back home, but you can embrace the journey, and with the right perspective, you might find out you can never really leave, either. Whether you acknowledge it or not, the thread of your parents' essence lives within you both in form (genetics) and spirit (mind/heart).

Don't discount your story as you return home and begin to confront the new paradigm in your life—taking care of your aging and dying parents. Also don't feel alone and isolated, as you're playing out one of the oldest stories of the ancient Gods—one that has been repeated by billions over millennia.

Happiness & Health

MHS

Made in the USA
San Bernardino, CA
23 June 2020